CW00419537

'Jesse, are you hurt?' Crystal heard her own teeth chattering and knew that they had to get out of the water.

'Jesse?'

She was terrified when his hand dropped away from hers, then finally he whispered, 'You've got to get us to shore.'

'Me? Me get us to shore? You've got to be kidding!' He would not open his eyes. 'Jesse, I can't! I don't know how to—for God's sake! I'm a tax auditor, not a weight-lifter! I can't get a big lug like you to shore!'

His eyes opened and somehow he managed a grin. 'I float in salt water,' he said raggedly. 'You can do it.' Then the black eyes closed, shutting her out, and he whispered slowly, 'I got us out of the plane. Your turn now.'

Books you will enjoy
by VANESSA GRANT

TAKEOVER MAN

Maggie was finally independent, working as harbour manager of a wharf and supporting her daughter, Dixie. They even had a kindly old man on the next boat, whom Dixie called Grandpa Angus. But then Angus' son Michael, corporate takeover man, arrived, trying to take over first his father and then Maggie herself...

STRANDED HEART

After having one marriage go sour very publicly, Nicole was wary of getting involved again. So the last thing she needed was Matt Kealy—who had no plans to stay in one place for long. Especially when he remembered the scandal of Nicole's past...

AWAKENING DREAMS

BY

VANESSA GRANT

MILLS & BOON LIMITED
ETON HOUSE   18-24 PARADISE ROAD
RICHMOND   SURREY   TW9 1SR

All the characters in this book have no existence outside the imagination of the Author, and have no relation whatsoever to anyone bearing the same name or names. They are not even distantly inspired by any individual known or unknown to the Author, and all the incidents are pure invention.

All Rights Reserved. The text of this publication or any part thereof may not be reproduced or transmitted in any form or by any means, electronic or mechanical, including photocopying, recording, storage in an information retrieval system, or otherwise, without the written permission of the publisher.

This book is sold subject to the condition that it shall not, by way of trade or otherwise, be lent, resold, hired out or otherwise circulated without the prior consent of the publisher in any form of binding or cover other than that in which it is published and without a similar condition including this condition being imposed on the subsequent purchaser.

First published in Great Britain 1989 by Mills & Boon Limited

© *Vanessa Grant 1989*

Australian copyright 1989 Philippine copyright 1989 This edition 1989

ISBN 0 263 76281 5

Set in Times Roman 10 on 11½ pt. 01-8904-55497 C

Made and printed in Great Britain

This book is dedicated
to the memory of my stepfather
William Angus
who spent his life
working on floatplanes
and loving his family

and to Lori, with thanks
for sharing her knowledge

CHAPTER ONE

FOR A second, as she came through the door into the unadorned office, she had the impossible thought that the man behind the counter was David. The illusion was fleeting, a product of that first glimpse of the stranger's dark, luxuriously curling hair.

When he looked up, her heart slowed. Of course it wasn't David. The stranger's shoulders were harder, broader, and he would be taller when he stood straight. David had been dark and tall and sleek, competent in city ways, but this man belonged to the strange wild and the outdoors.

'What can I do for you?' He sounded busy, but friendly. The eyes were black, not David's warm brown, and he was tougher, the lines of his face cut deeper by the easy smile.

He liked women. That was in the smile, in the black eyes as they scrutinised her tailored tan slacks and her tweed jacket. He took in her hazel eyes, her soft auburn curls. She had an uncanny feeling that he knew she went to the salon every month to have the hair carefully trimmed to shoulder-length. Did he know she would come just to his shoulder if she stood close beside him?

His inventory paused at her black audit-bag. Too big for a briefcase, too small for a suitcase. City girl, the black gaze said, seeming to emphasise that he was a northerner and she wasn't. She stiffened a little despite his warm interest, although she admitted to herself that if she were staying around in this hick town, and if he asked her out to dinner, she might just accept. There

7

was something about him that made a person want to
say yes.

She shrugged that discomfiting thought away and put
down her small suitcase. 'I'd like to charter a seaplane
to the Queen Charlotte Islands.' She shifted the audit-
bag, saw him noticing that she didn't put it down.

'Not likely this afternoon.' His voice was mildly re-
gretful, pleasant. His pen shifted and he glanced down
at a large sheet of paper filled with numbers. As soon
as she turned away, he would be working on those
numbers again. Not money figures, she knew that. Some
kind of inventory records? Behind him, a speaker
crackled and a youngish man hurried to pick up a
microphone. The man who was not David said, 'Where
on the Queen Charlottes? We've got a scheduled run to
Masset tomorrow at ten. If you want, I'll put you down
for tomorrow.'

'I have to get there today. Queen Charlotte City, not
Masset.' He frowned and she felt the day's frustration
mounting. More delays! Things had been going wrong
ever since dawn, and she simply must get out to that
little village before the sun set today! 'I've got to get
there today! I've already missed——' She quelled the
rising desperation in her voice. It was so unlike her, but
this day had been a disaster from the beginning. She
made herself smile at the man behind the counter and
was amazed at how her spirit warmed when he smiled
back.

His eyes passed behind her as a door opened. Heavy
footsteps crossed the floor, while on the other side of
the counter a young clerk approached with efficient
purpose.

'Jesse?' The clerk's voice was eager, younger even than
his face. Not-David gave a formless sound of ac-

knowledgement and the voice rushed on, 'Dalwyn says they can get those parts to us by Friday.'

'Good. Place the order.'

Jesse. She filed his name in her mind, somewhere between the details of tomorrow's audit procedures and the telephone number for the woman who cleaned her apartment every Wednesday. He belonged there, not with David's memories. Behind her, a man cleared his throat just as a telephone rang. Interruptions were looming everywhere. Crystal quickened her persuasion, smiling at the man named Jesse.

'I know you don't want to hear the story of my frustrating day, but I really have to get to Queen Charlotte City today.'

He shrugged, his eyes going to the man behind her. 'Listen, you'd be better to wait for the run tomorrow. It's cheaper by far. If you're going to charter a plane all for yourself, to go all the way to the Charlottes——'

She took a tighter grip on the audit-bag while pushing a frantic hand through her hair. His eyes caught in the auburn richness of her curls, but she didn't notice. 'I don't—— Look, can you just tell me if there's any way you can get me there today?' Her voice was biting in its frustration. Damn! She hated being inefficient, but the way things were shaping she was never going to get to this audit review. 'If you can't take me, I'll go check the other seaplane companies. I'm not worried about the cost, I just——'

The door opened again. A quick, slender man burst through it and rushed to the counter. 'Express for you! Consignment for the *Julie II*.'

'Good! We've been waiting for it.'

The courier pushed a paper across the counter. The dark man gave the parcel a comprehensive glance, then quickly signed the receipt. Through the open doorway a rising noise filled the air and made conversation impossible. Crystal swung around in time to see an amphibious aeroplane taxiing through the water towards the floats on the other side of the road.

'What about that plane?' Her voice was rising, attempting to organise a situation that seemed to be frustratingly out of her hands. 'It's just coming in, isn't it?' She swung back. The courier was gone, dashing back out of the door and into a small van. Jesse Whatever-his-name's black eyes were hard, as if she were pushing when he did not like being pushed. 'Can't I go to Queen Charlotte City in that plane?'

'You can't afford it,' he said flatly.

'How would you——'

His voice had lost the friendliness. 'Bruce, what's the charter rate for the Goose to QC City?' The clerk punched some keys on a calculator and came up with an answer that made Crystal swallow.

His voice softening, Jesse said, 'Look, the Goose is a big plane, too much for a single-passenger charter, and Queen Charlotte is a hundred miles away.' He frowned, then shrugged and said, 'Give me some time and I'll see if we can dig up something for you. You're sure you can't wait until tomorrow?'

'I'm positive.'

His eyes dropped to the audit-bag, seeming to lump the black mystery of it with her cool certainty. She could see the heavy shoulder muscles bunching under his shirt as he turned away. 'Why don't you go home—or back to your hotel? You're not a local, are you? I'll call you if I have anything available. It's kind of late in the day, but——'

'Jesse, while you're at it——' The voice that boomed out behind her was big and deep. She jerked around and found herself facing a burly native Indian who was saying, 'While you're at it, could you get me out to Kitkatla tonight?'

'Sure, Victor,' the dark man agreed easily. 'Got a Cessna coming in any minute now.' He picked up the small parcel from the counter. 'I've got to fly this part down to Butedale for the *Julie II*. Shouldn't be any problem to tack on a run to Kitkatla.'

She couldn't believe her ears. This was absolutely the limit, after everything else that had happened today. She exploded. 'Kitkatla is OK, but not Queen Charlotte? What does it take to get service around here? I suppose if I had a beard, I'd have no problem?'

The two men's eyes met in some kind of silent communion. She groaned. Here she was, hundreds of miles north of Vancouver, away from the city, and the macho males were closing in against the little woman. She felt her anger growing cold as Jesse said, 'Leave your name, I'll call you.'

Behind her, Victor said, 'What's MacDougal's problem? Is he broken down in Butedale?'

Jesse nodded, said over her head, 'Yeah. He called for a new waterpump, and we just got it in. If we get it down to him today, he can get out fishing while the salmon opening's still on.'

Crystal knew that if she left a name and number, if she went to a hotel to wait for his call, she would never get to Queen Charlotte until the scheduled flight tomorrow.

'What's your name?' he asked.

'Why?' She wavered a little under his black gaze, but kept her voice firm and cold. 'Why do you need my name? I'm paying cash. And I'm staying here until you've got a plane for me. A small plane.'

She was aware of the heavy presence of the Indian behind her. In front of her, Jesse unexpectedly grinned, startling her with sparkling dark eyes beneath that unruly thatch of dark hair. His smile showed deep lines that she thought were from his laughter. 'Because,' he explained patiently, 'when the plane crashes and you're killed, we need to know whose name to give the cops.'

Laughter boomed out behind her. She swung around and found herself staring at the burly Victor. He was wearing a thick mackinaw that made him even larger. For a second she felt terrified, then she took in his warm eyes and friendly grin.

'Are you going to give me your name?' persisted Jesse. 'Or do you want to cancel the request for a charter?'

'Crystal Selwyn.' Her own dark eyes were flashing as she said sweetly, 'I hope you enjoy having a joke at my expense. Do tell your boss that I think you've got a lovely sense of humour.'

Victor said in gruff tones, 'Lady, Jesse is the boss.'

Damn! He would be. She didn't know what perverse devil had made her start this silly scene, but she felt like an idiot between these two men. 'Look, can I get a plane or not?'

'Maybe——' Jesse looked suddenly tired as he turned away. 'Bruce, what's on for that Cessna after I deliver the part to MacDougal?'

The clerk rustled paper. 'Nothing tonight. Tomorrow morning it's booked for a pick-up at Bella Bella.'

'OK, then, Miss Selwyn, the Cessna's due back in about twenty minutes.' He glanced at his watch. 'Another twenty minutes to refuel, then I'll fly you myself—if you don't mind taking a detour first. I've got to fly Victor here down to Kitkatla, and the parcel to Butedale, then I can take you.'

'Thanks, Jesse,' growled the Indian at the same time as Crystal said, 'It's Ms Selwyn.'

He smiled at the native and ignored Crystal, turning away to tell the clerk, 'It'll be dark not long after I land on the Charlottes. I'll lay over there, and do the pick-up at Bella Bella in the morning on my way back.'

He wrote something, then snapped the book closed. 'Any objections?' He was smiling again and she thought that after the flight he just might ask her out to dinner, if the little town they were heading for had such a thing as a dining-room. Crazily, despite her recent irritation, she felt almost sorry that she would be too busy to accept. This evening would be spent working with her partner, catching up on today's missed hours, getting her working papers in order for tomorrow's heavy workload.

'Of course I've no objections. I appreciate your re-arranging things for me.' He turned away, and there it was again, that fleeting resemblance to David.

She took one of the uncomfortable seats for waiting passengers. Her hand went to her audit-bag, then fell away as she remembered. In keeping with every other event on this hopeless day, her tiny computer had somehow not taken a full charge when she'd plugged it in last night. On the plane from Vancouver she had taken it out and settled down to work her way through the hour-long flight, only to find the low-battery indicator flashing at her. She had turned then to preparing new working papers, but found her automatic pencil was out of leads and the spare leads were mysteriously absent.

If she knew how long it would be until her flight, she could take a taxi to an office supplies store, if this town had an office supplies store.

On the other hand, if she left, the man named Jesse might just fly away and leave her trying to reschedule a week's work because of one missed plane.

So she sat still, listening to the sounds of a charter seaplane office and waiting, hiding her impatience. There was a radio somewhere behind the counter. She could hear static, bits of conversations that were only partly sensible.

Pilots checking in with the base... the young clerk seemed to do most of the radio work...Jesse's last name was Campbell. Jesse Campbell. He had a confident voice, the friendly ease of his tones concealing efficiency. Bruce, the clerk, relayed a pilot's message about a mechanical failure. Jesse Campbell had the situation organised instantly, a spare part put on another flight, a phone call placed to the pilot's wife to let her know that her husband was safely stranded in some unpronounceable bay for the night, but was warm and comfortable in the fishing camp bunkhouse.

Someone came in through a back door. From the conversation she overheard she assumed it was the pilot of the Goose she had seen landing. He was finished for the day and was heading home. Like everyone, he seemed on friendly terms with his boss, although his voice revealed respect too.

He was talking on the telephone now. 'Lucy?' His voice warmed, dropping so that Crystal could barely hear it. 'Listen, I'm going to be away tonight—— No, Queen Charlotte.' He was talking to a woman, that was in his voice. Lucy. Lucille. He laughed, said huskily, 'I won't, I promise. I imagine I'll stay at the Sea Raven overnight. Look after the girls for me, will you? And I'm sorry about the dinner.'

Crystal got up quickly and left the building. Behind her, the wind caught the door and banged it loudly. She was uncomfortably aware that her face was flushed. Thankfully no one knew how intensely she had been listening in on his private conversation.

It might have been a girlfriend, but it was probably his wife who was to look after the girls for him. Crystal would remember that, and if he did ask her out to dinner she would freeze him dead.

The cool wind hit her with a shock. It had been warm in the waiting-room, but outside was a cool autumn day. She was crazy to feel so angry at a man who had smiled as if he were attracted. He probably smiled at all women like that. With his deep black eyes and the lush, curly hair, smiles could only be good for business.

It made no difference to her if he was married. She was passing through, and men were a poor second to her career. She had no time for men, for caring. The warmth and the love were in the past, and she had finally learned that life was simpler alone, that success was a better friend than love.

She crossed the street and walked down to the floating docks where the planes were tied. The Indian was there ahead of her.

'Friends in Queen Charlotte?' he asked, towering over her with both height and bulk.

'No.' The monosyllable seemed terribly abrupt here in the open air, with the bustle of seaplanes and people all around, the cool, blue autumn sky overhead. 'I'm going over there on business.'

She never liked explaining her job. People tended to become nervous of her, or to ask uncomfortable questions. This man didn't ask, but simply said, 'You'll like the trip. Pretty country.'

She looked around. Except for the seaplanes and a few buildings, all she could see were untouched mountains. She thought of flying alone with the pilot through all the wilderness to a remote village somewhere between Prince Rupert and Japan.

'There's the Cessna.' Victor was shielding his eyes against the sun, looking at a tiny thing perched on two floats. She swallowed nervously, wondering if it was big enough for the three of them. She was going up in that? Victor asked, 'Ever been on a seaplane before?'

She shivered and said tightly, 'No. Just jets.'

'Jesse's a good pilot. The best. You'll be fine.'

She had better be! She turned away, concentrating on the larger twin-engine planes that were big enough to take a couple of dozen passengers. No wonder it would have cost a fortune to charter one over a hundred miles!

Well, she was committed. No way out. She simply had to get to work before tomorrow morning, and there was no other way. No roads. No jets except the one she had missed from Vancouver this morning. A ferry a couple of times a week, but not today. It had to be the seaplane.

She watched the pilot tie the Cessna's pontoon to the wharf. A lanky, blond man started to put fuel into a tank in one of the wings. She had never been on any plane smaller than a Boeing 737, but she tried to tell herself that her stomach felt queasy only from hunger.

She had skipped lunch on the jet from Vancouver to Prince Rupert, too tense from the nonsense of missing her scheduled flight to the Queen Charlottes. She had spent most of the morning trying to find some other way to fly to the place she had to go to and being frustrated at every turn. Then some bright travel agent had come up with the idea of flying to Prince Rupert and chartering a seaplane. An insane notion, obviously!

When she got home to Vancouver, she was going to buy two alarm clocks, and set both of them every night!

She watched the refuelling operation absently, her auditor's training noticing that it would not be hard for someone to steal fuel without it being traced.

'If you want to come up to the office, Ms Selwyn, we'll get the paperwork out of the way.' It was Bruce, a pencil stuck behind his ear and a denim jacket zipped against the cool afternoon.

She paid, obtaining a receipt for her expense claim. With professional interest, she watched the paperwork Bruce processed. Whoever had set up the control system in the office had done a good job of it, better than outside.

All in all, she thought that this charter company was an efficient operation, although she could give the owner a few tips that would—she shrugged the thought away, wondering if Murray wasn't right, after all. She was getting so involved with her work that she had lost touch with herself, with Crystal the woman.

When Murray had made that accusation, she had argued that it wasn't so. Murray had insisted that her love-life was non-existent, that the men in her life were meaningless to her, cast off whenever they threatened to touch her real, vulnerable self. She shrugged her absent friend's words away and went back outside.

By the time she got back down to the docks, Jesse Campbell was there, the door to the seaplane cabin open and Victor climbing in.

'Want the front seat?' Victor seemed to assume that she did, because he climbed into the back.

Jesse took a firm grip on her arm and steadied her as she climbed up into the cabin of the plane. She was thankful to be wearing loose trousers rather than a skirt. Small! God, it was small! She fumbled, finding the seat-belt and fastening it with shaking hands. When she heard it click, she looked up and saw Jesse's eyes on her hands. She clenched her fingers together to stop the shaking, hoping that he would not say anything.

He sat in the pilot's seat, his arm brushing hers as he settled into position. He was wearing a heavy jacket over a soft flannel shirt, blue jeans on his legs, sturdy boots on his feet. He smelled of the outdoors. She concentrated on the feel of his presence, the fresh, clean smell

of his maleness—anything rather than think that this tiny
tin enclosure was going to take her up into the sky!

His hands and eyes travelled over the instruments. She
followed his motions, not knowing their meaning.

'Breathe slowly and deeply,' he said, his voice casual
in the cockpit. 'You'll find the flight quite noisy, but
that's normal. Nothing to worry about.' He grinned, his
eyes glancing off her, then back to the instruments. 'They
don't do much to soundproof these planes.'

He had a very nice smile. She forced herself to relax
a little. 'Don't worry, Mr Campbell. I'm not going to
faint, or scream. I'm not the type.'

His eyes dropped to the audit-bag tucked behind her
feet. It was a little large for the place she had put it, but
she had refused when he'd offered to put it in the luggage
compartment with her suitcase. Remembering, she
tightened her lips and saw him shrug, smiling a little as
if he had the feeling she did, that they were carrying on
an inaudible conversation behind the real one.

He reached for a radio headset, pulled it down across
that curly dark hair before he closed the door to the
Cessna. She had an odd urge to reach out and smooth
the hair where it stuck out from the pressure of the metal
headphone band. 'You're not the screaming type,' he
agreed, 'but there's no need for you to be frightened
either.'

He moved his hands and the engine fired into life, a
noisy intrusion. Strangely, she felt a little more relaxed
as Jesse manoeuvred the Cessna away from the dock
and out into the open channel where he could taxi.
Perhaps it was his low voice explaining confidently,
'We'll be flying to Kitkatla first—that's a village on an
island a little south-west of us. It's a very pretty inlet.
I'll be giving you some spectacular scenery for your
money. You'll see when we circle to land. After that,

we'll follow the channels south to Butedale. That'll be a quick stop. The fisherman who's expecting this parcel will be waiting for us in his dinghy. We'll be off again at once, then fly west to the Queen Charlottes. We'll arrive shortly before dark.'

'Do you always follow the channels instead of flying over the land?' She had to shout now to be heard.

He nodded, opening the throttle. The engine roared and the small seaplane powered through the water, accelerating, lifting. The take-off was so smooth that she didn't know they were flying until the plane banked slightly.

Jesse was making movements, adjustments to the controls. She could see the dark hair on the back of his hand as he reached overhead to adjust something. How did he get so tanned up here in the town they called the City of Rainbows? She wanted to ask what he was doing to the controls, but then she looked down, straight down along the underside of the wing, and saw the water twisting, angling away.

Breathe slowly. Slow and steady, he had said. She did, and after a moment they flattened out and she realised that her fingernails were digging into the palm of her right hand. She made her fist relax.

How long? She glanced at her watch. They hadn't been in the air more than five minutes. Queen Charlotte City before dark. When was dark? It was four in the afternoon now. Late September. It got dark earlier in the north in winter, didn't it? How long? Two hours?

Could she stand it for two hours? Sitting still, looking down, feeling the sides of the plane close around her, as if she were flying high in a little bubble.

The plane started to bump and toss, shuddering and destroying her semi-calmness. What if they crashed? What if——

She jerked as Jesse's hand covered hers. 'What?'

He pointed ahead. Above the Cessna's engine, she could just hear him saying, 'There's Kitkatla. We're circling once before we land.'

Below, land and water were spread out in an intricate pattern. Where he had pointed was a large, complex inlet cut into an even larger island, small squares that must be houses dotting one side of the inlet just inside the entrance. It looked like a wilderness of trees and black water down there, with only a few houses, a pretence of civilisation. What if they crashed on landing?

She twisted around in her seat, the seat-belt coming tight. Behind her, she could see Victor turned towards his window, looking out at his home village. He looked as casual as a man riding in the back of a car. She thought of the ride she took each day, the car pool from her apartment to the office on Pender Street. It seemed a million miles from this wilderness, but this plane was hardly bigger than the cars she rode in.

The wing-tip dipped down and pointed to the ground. The plane banked steeply in a turn that left her dizzy and terrified. It seemed that they would slip down along that pointing wing-tip to a crashing landing . . . the end.

Everything went silent.

The world was level again, but coming up fast. She could see water ahead, not so far down, and houses, quickly closer. And silence. Had the engine quit? What was wrong?

Jesse's face was intent, his eyes seeming to search ahead, taking everything in. His body was relaxed, moulding to his seat, and as his fingers flexed on the stick she had the feeling that the man and the aeroplane were one, united, working together.

Then her ears picked out the sound of the engine again, muted, but still ticking. Then louder as he touched a control with his hand. It seemed everything was as it should be. She held her breath, watching the water rush closer, knowing it would be over in a minute. They would be on the water, safe. Or crashed.

At first she did not feel the pontoons touching, then abruptly the ocean seemed to cling to the pontoons, dragging back on the seaplane and making it bounce in the water.

They were down. Safe.

If only her computer were working! If only she had pencil leads! Then she could work her way through the next take-off, work as they flew on. Anything to pretend she was somewhere else, not hundreds of feet up in a little crate that felt like a toy.

She tried to concentrate on the way Jesse manoeuvred the seaplane on the water, roaring across the inlet and up to the floats where Victor could disembark. It was hard to think about those details when her mind was trembling at the thought of the next couple of hours.

He was good at it. He did it every day, and his face was calm, his legs lying parted, relaxed, feet touching controls she did not understand. And, damn it, he knew she was afraid. She could feel his unobtrusive scrutiny, hear his carefully soothing tones when he spoke to her.

'All right?' he asked as he climbed back into his seat after paddling the seaplane away from the dock.

'I'll get by,' she said tightly.

'Of course you will.' His voice was casual, his hand reassuring as it unexpectedly touched hers. 'Think of it as a long commuter run,' he said, as if he had been reading her thoughts earlier.

'I'll try.' She shrugged, uncomfortable with his invasion of her fear. She would have preferred to conceal her emotions, keep them private. 'Don't worry about me. I'm tough.'

That seemed to amuse him. He fastened his seat-belt, looked down at her lap and saw that her belt was still tightly secured. Then, when he turned to look out his window, for a second she saw—again—the back of David's head.

This time the take-off did not panic her quite so much. She knew what to expect, and it was the same. She concentrated on the dials in front of Jesse when they left the water. On one dial she could see a small replica of an aeroplane turned as if banking. She stared at it until it was level, then watched the instruments for a few more seconds, not looking through the window until she was sure they had finished banking and turning, and were flying straight and level.

It wasn't too bad as long as he kept the thing level. It was this business of wing-tips pointing at the ground that really panicked her.

They rose up gradually, leaving the island behind, flying along at hilltop level until they entered a long, narrow channel. 'Grenville Channel,' he told her, as if he could hear her wondering. It went on and on, narrowing as they flew south. They flew over tiny boats, but the boats and the water seemed to be far below them, tiny toys. She felt as if she were above the world and had a special view, as if she were somehow remote from it all, remote even from herself. This sensation was new to her. In jets she usually worked or read a book. She seldom thought about the flying.

Looking down on the lush green shores of the long channel, she felt the barrenness of her own life, as if her career was nothing and the thing that mattered was the lonely nights, the breakfasts alone. She blinked away the tears, the memory of her baby Johnny.

'Where are we?' she asked suddenly, then shouted the words louder, because Jesse had not heard.

'That's Wright Sound—that body of water ahead.' He pointed and she nodded. She didn't care, but she tried to pay attention when he said, 'We'll be crossing the sound, then flying down Princess Royal Channel—another long, narrow one, but we only go about forty miles before we get to Butedale. After that——' He grinned. 'Then I'll take you where you want to go.'

The day was never going to end, and it was a bad day. If she could only endure, get through it, tomorrow would come and she could get her life back to normal. Tomorrow there would be work, and she was good at her job.

At work she could regain the feeling that she controlled her own life, not this crazy feeling that some mischievous God was turning her world upside-down with alarm clocks that didn't ring, computers that wouldn't work, missed planes.

And the man, the dark curls that made her fingers remember the feel of loving, touching... David. No, those dark eyes and the lined face were certainly not David's, yet they were disturbingly intriguing.

Eventually the drone of the engine lulled her thoughts to nothingness. The hills were high and green, one much like the next. The water was black, with white dashes and the occasional small toy boat. Ahead, there were clouds. She watched and decided that they were flying lower, below the tops of the hills, well under the clouds that had appeared.

Jets flew above the cloud cover, but a small plane like this would be obliged by regulations and safety considerations to keep visual contact with the ground. She wondered why the clouds and the change in altitude did not worry her, but decided the noise and vibration were making her feel odd, separate from what was happening around her.

Then the silence screamed, everywhere.

This was deeper, more total than the quietness that had frightened her on their landing at Kitkatla. She wasn't sure if it was imagination or not, but she thought she could hear the air rushing past the skin of the seaplane.

The tension in the man beside her was not imagined. He flicked a switch, then another. His eyes were everywhere, looking at the instrument panel, then out, then down.

The plane banked gently, silently, at his touch and the silence grew. His hands were busy even as he pulled the microphone closer to his lips. He said a series of numbers and letters, then, '—engine failure. I'm setting down at the north end of Princess Royal, near the west shore of the channel.'

They were going to crash. She felt frozen, as if it weren't real, but the water was floating closer and the silence went on for ever.

'We're landing. Down there.' His voice didn't register on her mind until he said, 'Crystal!'

She jerked, her heart hammering into her ribcage. The trees were close, too close, now. 'What? Is——' She couldn't finish. The silence was terrible, the ground growing horribly close. How could it take so long to crash? Her fingers clenched agonisingly on the strap of her audit-bag. Whatever happened, she had to look after the bag!

'It's all right.' He sounded calm, impossibly so. His face was still tense, but not panicked. 'There's no reason it shouldn't go well.' His eyes were on the water, not on her at all. Amazingly, he managed a laugh. 'This might not be my smoothest landing, so just put your head down between your knees and——'

'I know. I will.' She had read it in enough books. She assumed the crash position, head down, hands above her head. She couldn't see anything except his muscled legs through his jeans. It went on for ever, silence.

What had happened? Why had the engine stopped? Silence. How much longer? It surely couldn't be more than seconds, but it stretched to for ever. The plane seemed to keep flying, quiet, without power. She could see his legs, muscles bulging as he pressed on one of the pedals on the floor. What was he doing?

God! She was numb with terror, but he looked relaxed. This end of him, at least. She turned her head and let her eyes wander up to his thighs, the seat-belt across his hips, the bulge——

She jerked her head back, closing her eyes. Was she insane? They were crashing. In seconds she might be dead, and here she was looking at the pilot as if——

Then it all came from where it had been hidden, the memories flooding back until she could not tell which feelings were now and which then. Sliding, twisting. Johnny's sudden scream. David, his hands on the wheel, his face suddenly hard and tense. Long, long seconds.

'Only a few more seconds.'

The voice, so unlike David's, jolted her back. What was that sound? Water? Waves?

'Damn!' Her head jerked up as he swore abruptly. She saw his hand yank hard on the stick. Somewhere, someone shouted, 'Get your head down!'

She did.

Then the world went wild.

CHAPTER TWO

HIS hands were at her waist and for a crazy, upside-down moment she thought he was touching her in passion. Then she felt the seat-belt release and herself sliding sideways into the door on her right.

She twisted wildly to grab the audit-bag. Her eyes took in trees, water, the crazy angle of everything, but made no sense of anything.

Then there was the man, standing on his pilot's seat as it sank into the water, his arms pushing up on his door, his face rigid and determined. Insanely the door opened upwards, moved slowly as his muscles bulged.

More water flooded in, a white, foaming sheet of salty wet. Salt on her lips, foaming green and white over her pale, immaculate slacks.

'The computer! The files!' She jerked on the audit-bag, but the water was everywhere.

'Come on!' His hand was an iron band around her arm. She pulled on the black bag, using its weight to help her resist, but he only yanked harder. 'No! Let go of it! Get out!'

He found a foothold, braced himself on parts of the plane meant for hands, not feet. Then he leaned down over her like a threatening hulk and tore the bag from her hands.

'My audit-bag!'

His fingers gripped her wrists mercilessly and she was lifted, flailing, from the seat, borne up and up. She opened her mouth to protest again, choked on stinging seawater. Then she was sitting, balanced in the open doorway of the plane and everything was wrong.

The plane was lying tilted backwards, canted sideways in the water. As she blinked the water away from her eyes, everything gave a sickening lurch. Her legs sank into the water. Her wrists were still held painfully in Jesse's grip as she flung herself against him.

'We've crashed! We're sinking! I've got to get the bag out!'

He shifted, one arm holding her, then jerking her as if to wake her. 'Can you swim?'

'I——'

'Can you?' She nodded mutely, wanting to turn into the security of his arms as he pushed her away. 'Over there! There's a log! See it? Swim for it!'

She was still clinging to him as he pulled her tweed jacket away from her, stripping it off her arms as the plane gave another gurgle. Then he pushed her, hard, dumping her into the cold water.

She twisted, disorientated as icy water filled mouth and nose and eyes. Choking and sputtering, Jesse's shouted, 'Swim!' somehow made her arms move and she was going away from the sinking plane, her mind now concentrated only on the log.

Where was it? It had been dark and long, a large thing barely seen as Jesse pointed. God, it was cold! Where was he? Why wasn't he here with her? Did he have the audit-bag? He mustn't leave it behind. She should go back and—why had he left her to swim alone? She twisted to look back, but then she saw the log, almost submerged, barely floating.

Her hand brushed something slippery and elusive. She jerked in the water, eyes fastening on a long, shiny plant of some kind. She could feel the slippery stuff clinging to her hand. Cold and slippery.

The log was only a stroke away. She reached and it wasn't there, and then the cold really hit her, ice growing in her veins. It slowed her motions, making it impossible to take one more stroke, to reach, to move...

Her eyes closed.

It was easier then, not seeing. Even the cold seemed to take on a formlessness. Everything dulled. She wondered if it had been like this for David and Johnny.

Today had been strange from its beginning, and now she knew why it was. She was going to die. Yet it made no sense that she should have been spared that other time, only to go now. No sense...nonsense...

She could feel an eerie warmth growing. She was floating, warm, burning wet lapping against her cheeks. Soon the water would penetrate farther, and that would be——

Pain intruded, and noise. Shouting. She squeezed her eyes shut, tried to drift back to the warmth, the comfort. It was so much easier.

A hard band around her chest, arms caught and pinned, pressure against her breasts, cold and invading. She knew it was him. Jesse. He was pulling her, shouting. She didn't care what he did, if only he would leave her alone and let her drift.

'Fight, damn you!' The grip shifted, slipped. 'Don't give up so bloody easily!'

She shook her head, but it was going, and the cold was the only reality. That and the man shouting, 'If you think I can get you in to shore, you're dreaming! Now wake up, or you're going to be dead in minutes!'

He shoved and she hit something hard. A rough protrusion scratching her arm. She clung, moving, instinctively jerking her left arm away to protect it from the painful bumps on the log.

A long silence.

Her arms were curled around the log, her face turned to it, as if it were a man's naked shoulder. Her body floated out, away from the log, the waves gently lifting, moving her cheek against the log, rubbing against the bare skin of her inner right arm.

Finally, she opened her eyes and he was there, inches away. He had one arm slung over the log, a dark duffel-bag cord wrapped around his inert wrist. His face rested on his arm.

He had not brought her audit-bag, just that duffel-bag. His face was wet, the dark hair plastered down against his forehead. He no longer wore the head-phones. His eyes were closed, the lines of his face smoothed with exhaustion. He was breathing in deep, quick gulps, as if he had exerted himself past his capacity.

Behind him, she could see the plane, or what was left of it. There was no body to it, no cabin. Only two pontoons, floating up out of the water, upside-down. There was nothing else but water and trees and green mountains, and the lonely white track of a jet miles overhead.

She wasn't sure why her hand left the log and reached out, except that he was the only life in this world. She needed to know he was still there, to see his dark eyes telling her it was all right. Yet when she touched him, her fingers pressing against the wet coolness of his shirt, he didn't move.

Her fingers pressed into the bulge of muscle beneath his shirt, the hardness of his male breast. Numb finger-tips, but she could feel his heart beating.

'Jesse?' It was a whisper, hoarse, teaching her that her throat was raw from the salt water.

He didn't answer.

She kicked her legs, twisting sideways, facing him with her fingers tangling in a handful of his shirt to hold her still.

'Are you all right? Jesse?' Silence. Then his free hand slid out of the water, covered her clenched fist. She felt a sagging relief, joy because she was not alone. She let herself relax, willing to wait for him to be ready to talk.

Thank God he had managed to get a call out on the radio before they crashed! She was not going to make it to Queen Charlotte City today, but at least they would be alive!

When the rescuers came, they would see the floating remains of the plane. It would not be long. Perhaps half an hour and they would be out of here, have dry blankets and be on their way—back, she supposed, to Prince Rupert. She must stay alert enough to insist that the rescuers get the audit-bag out of the plane and give it to her.

'We'll have to swim to shore.' His voice was so hoarse and low that at first she did not believe she had heard right. He was totally still, but his fingers had tensed over her hand in the effort of talking.

She licked her lips and tasted salt. 'We can't.' The shore was there, behind the remains of the seaplane. 'It's too far. I can't swim that far. Not in this water, in these clothes.' If he had not taken her jacket away, she would not have made it this far, to the temporary safety of the log.

She felt a shudder go through him. 'Jesse, are you hurt?' She heard her own teeth chattering and knew that he was right. They had to get out of the water.

'Jesse?'

She was terrified when his hand dropped away from hers, then finally he whispered, 'You've got to get us to shore.'

'Me? Me get us to shore? You've got to be kidding!' He would not open his eyes. 'Jesse, I can't! I don't know how to—for God's sake! I'm a tax auditor, not a weight-lifter! I can't get a big lug like you to shore!'

His eyes opened and somehow he managed a grin. 'I float in salt water,' he said raggedly. 'You can do it.' Then the black eyes closed, shutting her out, and he whispered slowly, 'I got us out of the plane. Your turn now.'

'I can't.'

'We won't last an hour in this water.' She could hardly hear the words, then there was only his body lying limp in the water. The one arm clinging to the log was the only sign of life in him. She couldn't feel his heartbeat any more. She stared at him and wondered how to do the kiss of life on a man floating in water. She touched his lifeless face, but there was nothing.

'Damn you, Jesse Campbell!'

She could have given up, let the water have its way, but now he had handed his life to her. She had to get them to shore. They wouldn't last long in the cold water.

She was no gold medallist swimmer, no life-saver, but there was this log, and if he could hang on to it perhaps she could somehow get it to shore. It had been easier when she was a child, kicking, swimming to propel a log. Or perhaps the log had been smaller and the need to move it less imperative.

She kicked steadily and futilely until she was exhausted; then, as she lay panting in the water, clinging to the damned skeleton of a tree, she realised that the log was drifting, moving slowly towards the shore.

Kicking harder didn't make the thing move faster. Progress was sluggish, the log determined to go at its own pace. Once Jesse opened his eyes and seemed to focus on the shore. 'Good girl,' he muttered approvingly before he left her again.

She said sourly, 'I thought the north was full of male chauvinists. You're not supposed to leave the little woman to get you out of life-threatening situations.' She almost thought she heard him chuckle at that; but then she looked and he was so deathly pale that she must have imagined it.

The shore seemed so close, yet it eluded her efforts interminably. Eventually the big log passed the pontoons of the floatplane and she thought fleetingly of abandoning the log for the metal skeleton. But what was the use? There was nothing to hang on to except the struts that held the pontoons. No shelter. No warmth. The cabin of the plane itself was underwater and she was not sure if she could succeed in diving down to get the audit-bag.

If it weren't for Jesse, she would have been underwater with the bag. She had frozen, wasting precious seconds that were needed to escape the sinking plane. He had got her out, saved her. Now it was her turn. Her legs were aching, burning with the cold, but she had to keep kicking. Hadn't she read that victims of shipwreck in the north usually died of exposure? Hypothermia.

Was she warming herself with the kicking, the attempts to move the log? Or was she losing precious warmth with her physical exertions? Warmth, radiating out into that cold water, making no difference to the water but sucking life from her.

There was no one whose life would be damaged by the loss of Crystal Selwyn, but Jesse Campbell had a woman named Lucy and the girls waiting at home. She shook herself, realising that she had stopped swimming, that her eyes were closing. Then she kicked again and felt something different, a rigidity to the log that had not been there before. The end of the long log had struck the shore. It was wedged in a crevice of rock. She had made it to shore, but now what?

'Jesse!' His eyelids did not even twitch.

He was losing his grip on the log. It was awkward, impossible. He was big, far larger than she was. She got his arm around her shoulder, the dark-coloured bag hanging down in front of her, still attached to Jesse's wrist by the cord. She wanted to get it out of the way, but she was afraid that it might be something important to their survival.

He was heavy. She kicked, clung to him and the log, the old scar on her left arm aching terribly. Somehow she made progress along the log, through the water, until her bare foot kicked painfully against something hard and sharp underwater and she realised that she had lost her shoes. They had been nice shoes. German-made, slip-on sandals that looked elegant and felt wonderfully comfortable.

She tried to ignore the pain of bracing her feet against the rocks, not to wonder about the sharp things under-foot. She leaned on the log as she lifted herself, then tried to get Jesse's lifeless body on to those rocks. The log shifted as she leaned on it, sinking a little, then shooting away from her, out to sea, throwing her off balance on to the jagged rocks.

Jesse!

Terrified of losing her grip on him, she grabbed for him and the rocks at once, ignoring the pain, pulling, thankful for a slow wave that made his body surge up and let her pull ... pull ... yank hard—— There! He was propped on a ledge, safe.

Safe? Lord, the man was unconscious, might have been injured horribly by this last business of crashing against the rocks. He might even be dead by now.

'Jesse? Jesse! Are you alive?' He didn't respond. He
didn't look much like the strong, virile man she remembered at the controls of that plane. She leaned towards
him and found herself tangled with the strap to that bag
he had brought with him. The cord was twisted and
twisted again, tangled around his wrist.

It took a while to free it. The bag itself was soft. She
pushed it under his head because it seemed wrong to
have his unconscious head lying against those jagged
rocks. Then she tried to figure out what she was going
to do next.

Above them, only a couple of feet away, was a grassy
flat area topping the rocks. Alone she could scramble
up to it, even in her bare feet, but it would be impossible
to get an unconscious Jesse up there.

She bent over him, slipped her arms under his and
held on to him, trying to lift, to bring his body up with
hers as she straightened. It was hopeless. He shifted and
groaned, and she had to let him sag back on to the rocks.
He was too heavy, and she was too weak. Even if that
bag contained a rope, and she supposed it might, there
was no way she could muster the strength to move him.

She felt a sharp discomfort in her thigh and looked
down at barnacles and seaweed all over the rocks. She
twitched, wanting to jump away from the slimy ocean
life, but restrained by her bare feet.

Was it her imagination, or was the water rising higher?
A few minutes ago when she had shifted Jesse out of
the water, on to the rock, the gentle waves had been just
covering his legs, his torso and head free of them. Now
the water was to his waist. The tide must be rising.

'Jesse, wake up!' He was not going to wake. He was
never going to wake up. 'Listen, you big lug! If you don't
wake up, you're going to drown here! The water's coming
up, and I can't lift you!'

Damn the man! She had done all she could. Lucy couldn't expect her to do any more. Lucy and the girls would just have to——

That wasn't fair, to put her between a woman and her husband's death. Hadn't she done this once already, on the wrong side of the accident? She had been the one left behind, alone.

The water was coming up. Soon he would be floating again. But that was what she wanted, wasn't it? To get Jesse up, higher, until he was on that grassy flat spot. And the water would help, if it only kept coming in. If she could only figure out a way——

She left him, scrambling up on to the grass. It was harsh green, with rocks between the blades of grass. Painful on her bare feet. She was wearing tights, but they were in tatters, certainly no protection. She couldn't think about her feet. She had to—what was that? A few feet away, a dull green tangled in the rocks.

A piece of coarse fishing net. She struggled and got it free. It wasn't exactly a rope, but it was something strong and it might help. It must have been discarded from a fishing boat, or washed overboard and lost. Perhaps the net had been caught on the rocks and cut free by a fisherman.

It was impossibly long, but she had no way of cutting it, so she dragged it free, over the bumpy rocks towards Jesse. If she could somehow fasten it to him, then perhaps she could drag him up as the tide came in. No, she couldn't pull him over those sharp rocks!

But he would die if she left him where he was, lying in cold water with night approaching. How long had it been? She couldn't see the sun for all the trees and the hills, but there was pink in the sky and still there were no search planes. She had forgotten about rescue in the struggle to get ashore, but now she remembered his radio call and could not understand why their rescuers had not come yet.

'All right, you macho man. You're going to be rescued, and I'm going to do it—somehow.' She worked with numb fingers to open the bag he had brought from the sinking plane. Inside she found a soft mass covered with plastic.

'Bags within bags. What are you up to, Jesse?' He didn't answer, of course, but when she ripped at the bag she had the answer. 'A sleeping-bag. And it's dry.' She looked at the sky. It would be dark soon, and there was no point pretending they would get out of here before night fell. They would appreciate the warmth of that dry bag later, but first she needed it to cushion Jesse's body against the sharp rocks.

She managed to lift him enough to get the bag under his shoulders. Then again, to slide the end of the slimy fishing net under him. She had thought that she could somehow get him right on top of it, then attach it to him and pull him up, slowly, riding on the net and padded from the rocks by the sleeping-bag. That idea was hopeless. He was too heavy and it was too difficult to manoeuvre. In the end she used the fishing net as a rope and looped it around him and the bag together, threaded through under his armpits and tied at the back. If she could get him moving, she thought the bag would shield his torso and head from damage by the rocks. His legs would have to fend for themselves.

She climbed up above him and pulled, making her arms ache but accomplishing nothing.

'If you would wake up, this whole thing would be simpler,' she called down to him, but he wasn't waking. She hoped to God she didn't hurt him with this crazy effort to get him out of the water.

There was a tree close by. Thankfully the net was long enough to reach. She got the net around the tree, but had no idea what to do next. Then she remembered seeing a documentary on rock-climbing. When the climbers held each other with ropes they had passed the rope behind their back and leaned back to pull, so that the pull was on back instead of arms.

She got a few inches of net pulled her way, and Jesse shifted upwards ever so slightly. Then she was stuck, couldn't shift her grip on the net without letting it go. She felt carefully with her bare feet and stepped back just a little. Then again, leaning back, pulling, holding the net with both arms and her back. It was slow, but it was working!

She almost sagged with relief when she saw his head coming up over the lip of rock, the sleeping-bag bunched behind it, between Jesse and the sharp rocks. Then, as she sagged, he started to slip back, and she stiffened and held tight just in time.

It took so long, but he was slowly coming more and more on to the grass. His head. His shoulders. He had twisted sideways, and she was so glad that she had thought of the sleeping-bag, because otherwise he would surely not have survived the battering on the rocks.

She felt the strain on her arms and back ease as his hips were pulled up on to the grass, but she was afraid to let go of the net. She shifted her weight and he did not move, and only then did she drop the net and run to him.

She bent down, her cheek against his lips. There was the faintest stir of air. He was breathing, but his skin felt so cold to her touch, his firm flesh icy and slightly rough from the day's growth of his beard. She shivered as she touched him, and knew that she was barely warmer.

The knot she had tied in the net had tightened as she pulled. It was impossible to get undone with her fingers fumbling and cold, with this weakness spreading through all her bones and muscles.

She reached for his pockets, feeling through the denim of his jeans, trying not to be embarrassed by this intimate invasion. She almost smiled when she realised that her cheeks were burning, that she was terrified he would open his eyes and make some comment about her wandering hands.

'I'm just looking for a pocket knife, Jesse—Mr Campbell,' she amended, wanting the reassurance of a more formal address. 'Don't all you men carry pocket knives? For skinning bears and such.'

Bears. Her hand froze, her eyes scanning the trees desperately. What if one walked out of the bush, a big black beast coming towards them, nose twitching, eyes——

'Left pocket...'

She hardly heard his whisper, but her hand went to the pocket and it was there, an oblong hardness nestled against the hard muscles of his thigh.

'I'm glad you can talk,' she whispered back, her voice shaking. 'I thought you might be dead.'

She slipped her fingers into the tight pocket, having to twist to get past the tight, wet denim, into the opening. She could feel his muscles tensing as she worked her hand in, then grasped the hard knife.

It was a monkey trap, her fist unable to get back out of the pocket although her hand had slid in without too much trouble.

'Not dead yet,' he said hoarsely, his voice a little stronger. He shifted a little and there was more room for her hand to retreat. 'I can still enjoy a pretty woman feeling me up... very nice.'

'You bastard!' She jerked her hand back, found it trapped again by the pocket. She slowed, got free, then found that his eyes were closed. As far as she could tell, he was unconscious again.

Her hands trembled as she cut the net free. She wished he would open his eyes. She pulled the net away. It was getting darker and she was getting colder, and he was obviously shocked and suffering from hypothermia. Neither of them would survive the night unless they got warm. Her fingers had found a lump beneath the drying hair on Jesse's head, and she suspected that was the reason he kept drifting off into unconsciousness.

'If you would wake up,' she promised him, 'I'd even forgive you for saying I was feeling you up.' Her fingers remembered the feel of his thigh, and that was strange because they were numb and senseless by this time. She muttered, 'There's only one sleeping-bag, so I hope you don't misunderstand what I'm up to, because somehow we've got to get warm.'

The sleeping-bag was damp by now, but not nearly as wet as his clothes. She pulled it away from him, spread it out on the ground and started trying to get him out of his clothes. He was unconscious, but she couldn't help the hesitation as her hands went to his belt. She had been married, but she had always been a reserved woman, and she had never undressed David.

'You'll never get warm in those wet clothes,' she told him as she fumbled his belt open. 'But I wish you'd wake up and do this yourself.' She slid the zipper open, pulled downward to try to peel the denim away from him, then stopped again.

She could almost close her eyes and pretend it was different, that he was awake, lying there with his eyes closed and his senses alive to her touch. She pulled and his hips were in the way, but he lifted a little and she could peel the jeans down, away from him.

Soon, he would reach up, and...

She shuddered, looking down on the long strength of his thighs, the bulge contained by his briefs.

'Jesse, this is not my thing,' she said weakly. He didn't respond, and that made it easier to do the rest of it, to pull the denim legs over his feet and draw the jeans away from him. His briefs were blue, and very brief. She swallowed and tried to concentrate on his face.

Next, his shirt and the jacket. She got the buttons undone, his chest bared, but then she was stalled. How was she to get his wet jacket and shirt off? She bent down, slipped her arms around him and held him close to her.

'Jesse, you've got to help me. Sit up. I've got to get your shirt off.' One arm seemed to tighten around her, but he made no move to sit up. She gave up on that and rolled him to one side, then disentangled herself and pulled the jacket and shirt free of one arm. When that was done, she rolled him to the other side and got the wet clothing entirely free.

'This is like undressing a baby, but a hell of a lot harder. You're not much help!'

She stared down at him, a naked man, covered only with his briefs and socks. She realised then that the sturdy boots were gone. He must have discarded them before he swam from the plane to the log. They would have made swimming almost impossible.

'I'll take your socks off, but you're going to have to sleep in wet underwear!' His eyes opened and seemed to focus on her, although dully, and she said wryly, 'There's a limit to what I'm willing to strip off a strange man. There, that's the socks. Now, could you please help me get you on to the sleeping-bag?'

It was useless to ask. He was gone again. Somehow she managed the job herself, pulling the bag over him and even getting it zipped up. He should have looked warmer then, but he didn't.

She left him there, took his clothes and spread them out on a bush nearby. It was so cold that she was pretty sure they would be just as wet in morning.

Cold. She shivered, the light breeze penetrating her wet clothing and her consciousness. Damn it! She was cold, too! Freezing. Her feet were bleeding and her arm hurt like hell, and there was no one here ministering to her, making her warm, caring about her.

She had to get the wet clothes off. Night was coming, colder and colder. Did it ever freeze at night in late September? She had a horrible feeling that in the north it was not only possible, but likely.

'Jesse?'

When his eyes were open she felt better, but he was terribly still in the sleeping-bag. She reached in and felt his skin. 'It's not a personal gesture,' she told him. 'I'm just checking on...on your hypothermia.' Her fingers pressed against his icy chest. 'It's not good, you know. You're terribly cold. You're supposed to start warming up.'

The numbness was growing. She could feel inside herself the deadly lethargy that had overcome her in the water. Until now she had been active, forced to move by the need to look after this big man. Now she was sinking quickly.

She fumbled with the buttons of her blouse, then her slacks. She was nervous of his naked body, but seduced by the thought of the possible warmth they might generate together. She hesitated, shivering, spreading her clothes near his on the bushes. Her bra was terribly wet, too, and in the end she shed it as well. People died of hypothermia, so warmth was a hell of a lot more important right now than modesty. And, regardless of what Jesse had mumbled as she felt in his pockets, he was in no state to notice if her breasts were covered or not.

She kept her panties on, a symbolic modesty at most. The water had made the flimsy undergarment transparent. She had no idea whether two people could really fit into one sleeping-bag, but she slid the zipper back and started climbing in with him.

'Jesse,' she said, lying beside him, not touching except at the knees. 'My back is out in the cold. I've got to cuddle up, but you can tell Lucy that it isn't personal. It's——' She shivered and exploded in an unexpected sneeze. 'Oh, damn it! Will you move your arms and let me closer?'

She twisted her way inside his arms, against the soft hair of his chest. She squirmed, trying for the zipper, to close it and trap whatever warmth they could make.

She could not reach, not without leaving his arms. His upper arm closed around her, his hand pulling her down, and she could feel the beginnings of warmth from him. She gave up then, let her body curve into his. When his leg slid over hers she turned closer, the warmth of their private places growing together.

'All right,' she whispered, turning her face to find a comfortable resting place against his shoulder. Her breasts were crushed against his chest and it felt good, the warmth beginning to grow everywhere. 'This is just for survival. I'm going to try to go to sleep now, and if there's any bears around—— If a bear comes walking out of those trees, will you please turn back into a macho he-man and do something to protect me? I'm terrified of bears.'

He did not answer. She wasn't sure if it was her imagination that his arm tightened around her, but she told herself it was real. It was either that, or convince herself there were no bears.

CHAPTER THREE

'JESSE?'

Her whisper echoed hoarsely through the trees.

She had woken suddenly, knowing danger was near. She had lain immobile, listening, hearing nothing. Even the soft rise and fall of the sea against the rocks was silenced. Overhead, the sky had cleared.

She had never seen so many stars in her life, brightly blazing. She had gone to shows at the planetarium in Vancouver, looked up at the impossibly false sky filled with stars overhead. Later, she had never been able to find any of the constellations, except the big dipper, of course. Now, with the heavens blazing overhead, she was sure she could find them all, if she could only remember the clues.

His arm was lying across her hips, slack and heavy. She was terribly glad he was there but, even more, wanted him awake and alert, ready to defend her from the thing that had made that noise.

She thought his breathing seemed easier, like the deep sound of a man sleeping. As he moved, his warm chest pressed against her shoulder while the stars blazed overhead. Was there another world up there, somewhere another woman lying under the open sky, wishing the man beside her would wake and defend her?

Again. The loud crack of a branch giving under something heavy. A rustle. Oh, God! A sound like breathing. A snort. It must be a bear, hovering around, getting ready to come over here and——

44

She turned into the broad, warm security of his chest. Outside was cold. She could feel it on her face. But here it was warm, a world inside the sleeping-bag, a world about to be torn apart by a marauding bear.

'Jesse!'

The thundering of her heart should wake him, but he did not stir. She turned closer to him, slipped her arm under his and burrowed as deeply into his chest as she could. His hand curved around her buttocks, drawing her still closer.

But he slept on, and she was so tangled in him now that, if the bear came to attack, she could never get loose to run.

'Jesse?' She pulled him closer with a jerk as another branch gave way to the beast out there. 'Please, Jesse! Wake up!' She was hissing, trying not to shout, not to disturb the thing in the bushes.

She pulled her arm free to touch his face, a futile attempt to rouse him. His arm settled more intimately around her curves, pressing against her breast, her waist, as he still held her close in his sleep.

'Jesse, there's something out there!' Her fingers pressed against the side of his neck. She could feel a pulse beating there, strong and virile. He must be all right. He must wake soon.

'Hm,' he murmured thickly, turning his head to her touch. 'Nice.'

Her fingers found their way into the thick, curly hair. Oh, damn! The man thought she was coming on to him, even in his sleep. It was almost funny! No, damn it! It wasn't funny! There was that noise again, and it was closer this time!

'Jesse, it's a bear! I'm sure it's a bear!' She twisted against him, found her breasts pressing into his chest, unwillingly felt the erotic sensation of his soft mat of chest hair brushing over her nipples. She could feel his deep sigh. The hand on her buttocks moved as his lips found her shoulder.

'No!' He didn't seem to hear. Was he awake? This was ridiculous! There was a bear out there, and this man was touching her, making love in his sleep. His lips were touching the softness above her breasts. It felt so——

'No! Please!' She tensed, pushing back from him with her arms. As she pushed away, her leg slipped through between his and she stopped, shocked by the sensations rushing over her as she felt his hard, masculine response to her nearness.

'Nice,' he murmured again, his voice husky in the darkness. His lips moved down and possessed the peak of her breast, setting off a surge of heat through her bloodstream. She could feel it everywhere, welling up, trying to burst free.

'Oh!' She gasped as his other arm slipped down under her, both hands cupping her buttocks now, bringing her closer, hard against him. 'Jesse! I——'

His response was a formless sound deep in his throat. One hand slid up over her panties to touch her silken skin, to explore the curve of her waist, the swelling that was her ribcage, then her breast.

He lifted the swelling to his lips, squeezing gently with long, strong fingers, touching his lips, his tongue, turning her to a shuddering, trembling mass of desire.

She dragged air into her lungs, was dully aware that her head was thrown back, inviting his touch, his kiss, anywhere he pleased. This was wrong. It wasn't like her. He was touching her, sliding fingers over her softness, pressing his hardness against her. She wasn't the kind of woman who——

Oh! His lips were on her neck, her throat, while his hand still possessed the growing swelling of her breast. Her tongue slipped out to wet her dry lips, leaving them parted for him. She moved her mouth closer to him, heart pounding, an invitation for the invasion of his tongue into the dark need of her mouth.

Sanity. She was an auditor, wasn't she? Rational. Sensible. No flings. No men, except dinners and shows. No going out drinking at parties, getting into compromising situations. Safe...safe....

It was her hand exploring the narrowing of his waist, the hard thrust of his buttocks, the lean bulge of his outer thigh. Her hand slipping down as he drew his thigh across her, slipping down and almost touching the hard ridge of his manhood.

Then his, covering her hand and holding it where her touch had hesitated. Then everything still. Her heart thundering. His heart crashing against his ribs so hard that she could feel it.

'You're awake?' She could only whisper, nothing against the surging desire she could feel flooding between them.

'I am now.' Husky, his voice heavy with desire. His hand slid down along the softly sheathed muscles of her back, then returned to the mound of her breast. He moved his head just a fraction of an inch, found her lips and took some of what was surging through her veins, just a small, shattering touch on her lips with his lips, his tongue, before he murmured, 'Lady, you could wake the dead.'

'I didn't——'

'Didn't you?' He moved against her hand. She jerked it away, only to find herself closer to him, their legs entangled and their heat touching through the thin fabric of her panties and his briefs.

And she did not want to pull away.

Was she crazy? There was something out there, in the bushes.

'Jesse, there's——' His thumb rubbed over the peak of her breast, sending a wave of need flooding through her veins, swelling the centre of her womanhood to aching sensitivity. 'There's—I think there's a bear out there.'

'Probably.' He didn't seem to pay much attention to his own words. He twisted and the sleeping-bag parted, letting in the cold air. 'Can't have that,' he murmured. 'Come over here.' He drew her close with one arm, used the other to fumble with the sleeping-bag. He must have found the zipper tab. She felt his muscles tense, hard against her, as he slid the zipper up and enclosed them together in a small space.

He was going to make love to her, and she realised that she was going to let him. The time to stop had been much earlier, before his lips had touched her, before his hand had caressed. Before she had touched him. The analytical part of her mind, usually dominant, tried to know why this was happening, but she knew only that she wanted him, that he had touched something that could not be denied.

Perhaps it was the near brush with death, crashing into the water, struggling to get them to shore. Or perhaps relief that he was alive and well. He had to be well, didn't he? There couldn't be much wrong with a man who was so definitely aroused.

He was very still, holding her close, but watching her, seeing only the shadows of her face in the starlit night. He was waiting.

'Well?' His question was quiet, clear, and she could hardly pretend not to know what he meant with his hand touching her where no man had since David.

Around them was only the silence. 'What about the bear?' It had been out there. Something.

She thought he smiled. 'We've got nothing for the bears to eat. They won't bother us.' His hand left her breast, slipped out of the bag to touch her face. He drew one finger down along the curve of her cheek. 'There's only you and I. We're the only two people in the universe.'

This was the moment to say no, to draw back. He was waiting, giving her that chance, so that she could never say he had forced her, had made it impossible to say no.

'I——'

His fingers traced softly the thrust of her cheekbone, the soft flesh under her jaw. The arm that lay under her was still, his hand withdrawn from intimate contact. He was waiting, but still touching her, still close, and no matter what happened next his touch would be with her all through the night. She was not fool enough to believe that either of them could survive the night outside this sleeping-bag. Her ears were tingling from the cold, although the rest of her was hot enough to heat a three-bedroom house.

He said, 'I want you, Crystal Selwyn,' his voice husky again, telling her that he would not wait much longer.

She stirred against him. 'I know.' He laughed and she could feel him, the muscles and the hardness and the heat. The fire was inside her, along with a fear that had not been there earlier. 'Jesse, I'm not—I don't——'

He found her lips, covered them gently, his tongue tracing the fullness and the trembling of her mouth. 'You pulled me out of the ocean. I don't know how you did it, but I'm glad you did, because I'm not ready to die yet, and I would have died out there.' She heard his soft laughter again, then his hand closed on her back, bringing her closer. 'I'm alive, and right now I feel more alive than I ever have in my whole life. Waking up like this, alive when I should be dead, my arms filled with a woman like you, all soft and firm and wonderful...' His husky voice was sending fire everywhere, his words insisting, 'I want to make love to you, and I think you want it too...now...tonight...under those stars.'

'Yes.' It was hardly a whisper, but he heard.

She loved the sound of that laughter, husky and low as he drew her closer, when closer seemed impossible. She had never known before that laughter went with loving a man. 'I'm glad you agree,' he whispered, low in her ear. 'Because I didn't know how the hell I was going to manage to hold you in my arms all night without making love to you.'

She felt a hot flush of embarrassment. Strange, after the last half-hour, that she should feel self-conscious now. She swallowed, knowing that the need between them was too deep to deny, but somehow afraid to touch him.

As if he understood, he loosed his hold on her, bent his head and took her lips in a slow, gentle seduction. His lips and tongue teased hers, hovered at the entrance without penetrating. His teeth took tender possession of her upper lip.

'You taste salty,' he told her, drawing his mouth away while hers was parted, needing.

'So do you,' she whispered, her lips tingling still.

'I'm going to lick all the salt off your skin.' His promise was roughly spoken, as if his own words made his voice unsteady. He bent down, his tongue licking softly the trembling flesh of her cheek, her neck.

'Everywhere?' She felt reckless, daring. David had been a silent lover, wanting silence. These words seemed excitingly wicked, words she could not have spoken within four walls. 'I'd like that.'

He tasted her neck, the roundness of her shoulder. She thought she would burst, waiting for the touch of his tongue on her breast. Then he found the hollow of her shoulder and she forgot everything but now, his lips searching an erogenous zone she had never known she possessed.

'I don't go to bed with men I don't know.' She hadn't known the words were coming. They must have burst from her subconscious, from Crystal the sensible woman. She hoped he would not listen, because she needed his touch, his kiss, his possession of her. Tonight she would be barren, more alone than all the other nights, if he did not take her, share his warmth, the strong virility that made her feel she could shelter, find safety.

He drew back, his lips parting. She could feel the hesitation, feared the darkness and the loneliness of lying quiet near this man, without his arms around her. She needed someone. Just for this once. Just one night. Not to be alone, to pretend life was warm and safe and shared with someone.

Her arms slipped up around his neck, drawing him close, his skin against hers. She bent and tasted the salty tang of his shoulder, found her lips lost in exploring the muscular ridges that led down to his chest, the hollows that quivered when she probed them with her tongue.

She felt his groan before she heard it, his hands drawing her close, hard against his need. 'Please,' she whispered then, her mouth against his skin, her teeth finding the male nipple that went rigid to her touch.

She groaned as he pushed her away, but her shoulders were down then, against the bag and the uneven ground below. And he was above her, blocking out the sky, parting her legs with his knee.

She was ready for him, needed him, but he stopped to bend down and take the peak of her breast deeply into his mouth, his tongue caressing, leaving her weak and hot and wet, her hands gripping, pulling him down.

Then he slipped inside and the heat exploded, the furnace blazing. Her eyes closed and she could see the stars, feel the universe speeding by as they moved together.

She heard someone whimpering and it was herself, but the sounds were not sense, only need and loving. He answered and she could feel the answer through her body, her bloodstream. She held him and he thrust harder against her, then there was only her head thrashing on the ground, his mouth taking hers deeply as he thrust, sending the stars spiralling until they burst, the heavens exploding, spinning down. Somewhere in that dizzy descent to shuddering fulfilment she felt his body go rigid, then the groan escaped him and he held her close, tight, prolonging the moment when they merged into one.

Afterwards, she slept, secure in his arms, the bears forgotten.

Amazing how being close to death made a man appreciate the good things in life. She was close in his arms, sleeping, and he could not remember ever holding a woman like this, feeling every breath she took and wanting nothing more than to feel the next.

He felt no desire. Not now. He could never remember a time when a woman had left him so spent and satisfied, but that too must be the brush with death.

His head was throbbing. He chuckled silently, quietly because she was sleeping. If his head had hurt earlier, he hadn't noticed. There had only been her. Crystal. Close and warm and damned desirable. He felt the stirring again but pushed it down. Perhaps he could rouse her from sleep with kisses, but this was good too. Holding and feeling her close, feeling the soft warmth of her breath against his chest.

Earlier she had somehow managed to get him to shore, to save his life. She was small, slender except for the voluptuous curves of her breasts. When he was loving her, he had felt the surprising firmness of her lean muscles, but still he had no idea how she had managed to get his bulk up out of the water, on to this grassy knoll.

He remembered his dive back into the cabin of the plane, an attempt to salvage enough in the way of supplies to keep them alive while they waited for rescue. His hand had grasped the sleeping-bag, his other hand searching for the kit that held flares and emergency rations, as well as the thin, silvered space blankets that could make a life-giving shelter, or a covering against the night.

He had found it, shifted to grasp, to pull the weight of the kit out, get himself free before his bursting lungs gave out. Then everything had exploded into stars and pain as his head collided with something hard and sharp.

It must have been the air trapped in the plastic-wrapped sleeping-bag that had taken him to the surface. He didn't remember the ascent, only a sudden spluttering as he choked on a wave of water, an awareness of his wrist tangled in the string that held the sleeping-bag.

Somehow, half-conscious, he had struggled to the log, grabbing at Crystal when he saw her, terrified because he realised she was giving up, and she seemed suddenly and irrationally like someone precious to him, too important to lose like this.

Then the dizziness had swept over him and he had barely managed to fling his arm over the log, the sleeping-bag dragging across and falling into the water at the other side. He couldn't seem to grip the log. His head was starting to pound dizzily, but miraculously the weight of the sleeping-bag seemed to hold him in position. He remembered the cold...then her hand on his chest...then nothing.

Until he woke to the warmth of her body against his, the woman who had saved his life bringing him fully to life, fully aroused.

She turned against him now, her small white hand gleaming in the moonlight as it spread across his shoulder. He shifted, covering her hand and his shoulder with the bag, keeping out the cold. It was his turn to look after her now.

The prospects weren't all that good. He hadn't managed to bring out anything but the bag. It was dark-coloured, as were their clothes. When daylight came, there would be boats passing by in the channel, but there wasn't a chance in hell of attracting their attention without the aid of a flare. The bush on shore was too dense, and the boats too many feet away. They could wave and shout and scream, but no one would see them.

Eventually there would be a search, but even that wasn't too promising. He tried to look out over the water, but he couldn't see the pontoons of the seaplane in the dark. The shores of this channel were very steep. There was little to stop the seaplane drifting with the current, and the current was swift. The floating pontoons would be miles away, and even if they were spotted, searching this shore was hopeless.

Damn! He had been on enough searches to know what it was like. How many times had they scoured the trees, knowing that the missing plane was within an area of a few miles, and not been able to spot the plane, much less the passengers?

And there had been that man down the channel last year. They had found his boat anchored, empty, the dinghy missing. Later they had found the dinghy drifting, only a mile away. Boats and planes had searched the shore for miles around and found nothing. Some idiot had suggested that they send out search parties into the bushes—a fool who didn't realise how impenetrable these bushes were, the undergrowth turning the forest into a wall of green.

Eventually the search had been abandoned. Then, amazingly two weeks later, the man had turned up in Kitimat. Alive. He had walked out. What had it been? Seven miles? Two weeks.

He wished now that he had taken the trouble to look the fellow up later. Why had it taken so long? The northern coast was terrible to walk through, but surely a person could manage ten miles a day. He thought he could do ten miles in a day, although he wasn't sure about Crystal. She was a city girl, probably soft and——

No, damn it! She had got him ashore without help, and had the sense left to strip off his clothes and get him warm. Then she had been sensible enough to forget her modesty and climb in with him; if not, she would have been the one lost to hypothermia. Any woman who could do all that could surely walk a few miles of bush.

Butedale was the best bet. The old cannery town was virtually abandoned, but even if there was no caretaker left on the townsite, there would be boats stopping, tying up overnight to what was left of the ruined wharfs.

He closed his eyes and tried to visualise his aviation chart of this area. Butedale. They were on the east shore of Princess Royal Island, a few miles south of the north end. Butedale couldn't be more than fifteen miles south. Perhaps a little less.

They would need something to protect their feet. He had had to unlace and jettison his boots before he dived into the sinking plane. Her shoes—he remembered back at the seaplane base, watching her walk away from the counter, looking at what he could see of her legs through the slacks. Some kind of sandal, he thought. They would have fallen off in the water.

He lay quietly through the night, holding her against him. His head did not stop its painful pounding, but he thought his brain was clear, so there must not be any serious concussion. Earlier, he had been unconscious, but now he thought it was all right. There might be dizziness in the morning when he tried to stand up. He flexed his muscles carefully, not wanting to disturb her sleep, but feeling for soreness, weakness. His left hip was bruised and his ribs were tender, but other than that he felt good. He drifted, sleeping lightly, snapping alert just before the sky lightened with morning.

It was going to be a good day, clear and cloudless. He knew from yesterday's weather report that there was a front hovering to the west, but their luck would hold for this day. There would be no rain. He hoped their clothes would dry in the morning sun, then they could start walking.

Luckily he had called Lucy before he took off yesterday. She would look after the girls while Charlie was away, so he didn't have to worry about that. Shoes were really the biggest problem.

Crystal stirred against him in the moments before the sun rose. He could see her face now, pale in the early morning light. Her lips were softer than they had been when she had walked into his office yesterday. He smiled, thinking how businesslike she had looked then; how sleepy and soft she seemed now. This morning's woman did not look tough enough to have managed to save his life.

He would have liked to wake her with his lips on hers, but this morning was a time for work, not play. Also, Crystal Selwyn's tousled body lying naked in this bag with him was so in contrast to her businesslike city image of yesterday that he thought she would wake embarrassed. He wanted to spare her that if he could.

He slipped away from her, almost wavering in his resolve when her hand reached out aimlessly to find his warmth again. He stood beside her, shivering a little in the cold air, looking down at the tumble of auburn hair that hid her head as she pillowed it in her arms. The curls parted across the back of her neck and he could see the faint line of an old scar.

Then he remembered his briefs, discarded in the night. He rummaged carefully, trying not to touch her but finding his fingers caressing her thigh. If he did wake her, make love to her in the morning, he could almost guarantee the timing for a rescue. That would make wonderful headlines! Pilot crashes, ravishes customer while waiting for rescue. He jerked his hand back, grinned, then chuckled, cutting his laughter quiet suddenly. If she woke, he didn't fancy having to explain to her what had seemed so funny.

His clothes were spread out on some salmon-berry bushes that were past their prime. Too bad. They could have used the berries, bitter though they were. He moved his wet jeans to where the sun would catch them, then spread out her clothes beside his. The thin blouse she had worn was badly ripped. He remembered her tweed jacket, wished briefly that he hadn't left it in the water, then shrugged the regret away and concentrated on things he could do something about.

He put on his shirt. It was wet, but he thought the sun and the heat of his body would dry it if he kept moving. There was lots for him to do.

She seemed to have slept for ever, deep and heavily. She woke with the languid feeling of a Sunday morning, then jerked up with a sickening sense of disaster.

She had missed that plane. She was supposed to be flying to the Queen Charlottes with her new audit partner. She hadn't worked with him before, which made it a tense situation in any case. It didn't help for her to prove herself inefficient on the first day.

Damn! She wasn't inefficient. She was good. Next year the manager of her field audit team was likely to be transferred. She thought she might have a good chance in the competition for his job, but not if she messed up like this! She had to catch that damned plane, get out there and——

The thoughts went on ahead of the signals from her eyes and ears. The alarm clock not set. That was yesterday. This was——

Wilderness. Bush. Water out there. Trees. She was naked, huddled in a sleeping-bag...alone.

Alone? She pushed a wild tangle of hair back. Oh, no! Surely it had been all a dream? All of it. The crash. The dreadful struggle to get the pilot to shore. She looked down at her burning hands, saw the lines where she had bruised herself pulling on the net, trying desperately to lift the pilot up out of the water, away from the rocks.

She had stripped him and wrapped him in the sleeping-bag, climbing in herself for warmth. There had been no choice. Then, later, the bear—if it had been a bear. The noise in the bushes, her attempts to wake him—Jesse—and somehow it had all turned to heat and passion and need. She'd gone up in flames. In her whole life she could never remember doing that, needing and whimpering and clinging, crying out with the joy and the almost unbearable agony of pleasure.

She was not on the birth control pill, or anything else for that matter. There had been no need since David had died. Even then, it had been David who decided there would be only one child, David who had gone to the doctor.

And last night nothing had been done. It had been wild, passionate loving, unplanned and unprepared for. She spread her fingers wide to feel her belly, and knew somehow that there would be a child.

It would be a healthy child, born with a full head of dark, curling hair. She shuddered, seeing the child, feeling it in her arms, turning to suckle. She thought Johnny would want that for her, another child to love.

No! What was this? Dreams awakening, as if she were a teenager. As if that were all there was to it, the romantic idea of having a baby. Didn't she know better than that? Dreaming dreams as if they came true, as if love wasn't hurt and loss. She shivered. It was cold. If there was a child——

Dreams were for dreamers, and she was no dreamer. Not any more. She wouldn't hope for it, but——

If it happened——

She made good money, had a stable career. Maternity benefits. And there were lots of single parents. She found herself smiling a little, her fingers curling, feeling a warmth inside her until the sun lifted over the trees and shafted brilliant light down on her.

Was she insane?

She pushed her hands down along her naked body, tried not to feel the fullness that remained from the flush of loving. She didn't know where the pilot was. Perhaps on the shore somewhere near, looking for a boat to rescue them. He would not be far.

She could feel the warmth from him still.

She gathered the bag tighter, twisted and found her clothes gone from the branch, looked farther and saw the polyester fabric of her slacks lying in the sun nearby.

She would get dressed before he came back. Then, soon, there would be a rescue. She hoped they found her audit-bag, otherwise she would have to report it lost. Confidential taxpayer files floating around for anyone to find!

How was she to get home dressed like this? She'd have to hide out in a hotel somewhere, get a co-operative ladies' wear store to bring her something. Use her credit card—— No, damn! No wallet. There would be all the mess of losing things. New driver's licence to apply for. Credit cards to report lost. How would she get home?

Murray. He would wire her some money and a ticket. Then she would be home, and she would forget last night.

Or would she?

She realised that inside her was the hope growing, that last night would bring her another child, and that the man who had fathered it would never know.

CHAPTER FOUR

WHERE was he? Had he abandoned her here?

She was alone, the sun shining down on her through the trees. She squinted and twisted in the sleeping-bag, but there was no one anywhere. A carpet of evergreen needles and gravel through scraggly grass...trees rising from a tangle of low bushes, all dark green, a sea of dark green everywhere she looked.

Except out over the water. It was still, empty. The seaplane was gone. It was daylight. Where was the rescue? Where was Jesse?

Last night he had been unconscious. What if he had concussion, had wandered off and got dizzy, fallen and was lying broken on the rocks along the shore?

She bit her lip and stumbled out of the bag, abruptly aware of her nakedness. What if he was watching? She grabbed frantically for her clothes. The trousers had a cold dampness that made her shiver even more. And her shirt was in tatters, damp rags hanging on her. She trembled and fumbled the buttons closed. She would not stay in that sleeping-bag, waiting for Jesse to come back as if she wanted his touch on her again, his lips kissing, his man's body possessing her.

The hell of it was, she did want just that, but it was morning now, and she had control of those crazy urges. She tried to tell herself it was funny, cool Crystal waking up hot for a man.

Would the baby be a girl? That might be best, not an active reminder of Johnny. Oh, God! Stop it, you idiot!

61

There wasn't going to be a baby! One night . . . just once. Not likely at all.

She wanted—— No! She didn't really want a child. It would be silly to tie herself down like that. She would have to look for a transfer out of active auditing, cut down on travelling. It would mess up her career. The apartment where she lived didn't allow children or animals, and she did not want it, so it was lucky there was almost no chance that it would be true.

Unless they were not rescued today, and tonight . . .

She didn't understand why the planes had not come yet. Rescue should have been here with the dawn.

What was that noise?

Jesse? Or the bears? She stared at the dark green of the trees, the shadows between. What was that dark lump? An old lightning-struck tree trunk? A bear?

That noise again. Jesse? She pulled at the tatters of her shirt. Would he come and expect her to—what would he be feeling? What about Lucy? Oh, lord! She had forgotten his wife, but she felt the guilt rising now. Last night she had needed someone, but how could she have let herself make love with a married man?

Her heart pounded, waiting for him, watching the shadowy bushes where she had heard the noise. A bear? The bear had attacked him, and was now coming for her! Should she try to climb up a tree? That tree, with the thick, knobby trunk and branches starting low. Or should she run down on to the rocks, into the freezing green water?

Thank goodness! It was him. She could hear a low whistling, vaguely tuneful. Bears didn't whistle.

Had they created a child last night?

Perhaps he was done with having children. David had gone to the doctor. Perhaps Jesse had done the same. She touched her stomach through the damp slacks and wondered how a woman asked a man about something like that? A strange man, because they had only met yesterday and hadn't spoken more than a dozen sentences to each other.

Jesse, are you fertile? She choked, knowing she could not ask, no matter how she phrased it.

The whistle was louder, as if he were warning her of his approach. She pulled at the blouse again, looked around desperately for something to occupy her hands. Her eyes fell on the dark sleeping-bag and she dropped to her knees and started to roll it up, as if she could hide the memory of last night.

'Good morning!' His flannel shirt didn't look as soft or as clean as it had yesterday in his office. Below the shirt his legs were bare. Her eyes shied away from the dark growth of hair along his thighs, remembering how that erotic roughness had teased her softness.

'Hi, I——' What on earth had she meant to say? What did you say to a man, half a stranger, the morning after he'd made love to you? A married man. 'How—how long do you think it will be before they get here?' She was making a mess of the sleeping-bag. She stopped, unrolled it and started straightening the folds. She brushed at the evergreen needles she had rolled into the bag.

'No one's coming here.'

He was standing over her, half dressed, his breath showing frosty. Her eyes flew to the jeans lying on the bushes. Denim took a long time to dry, but she wished he would put them on.

'What do you mean?' She looked out to the water, not at him. 'We'll be rescued. We——'

He reached down and grasped her arm, pulled her roughly to her feet. She jerked back, frightened. 'Hey, what do you think you're——'

'Listen to me, Crystal!' His eyes were blacker than last night, yet blazing hot. She strained against his hand on her arm. What was he going to do to her? He sounded so harsh, threatening. 'Get it straight right now! We can't afford to think that we'll be rescued. We'll rescue ourselves, or we'll die. That's it.' The lines of his face were cut deep. Her fingers curled, almost reaching to touch, to reassure herself that there was more to him than this hardness.

'No.' She shook her head, felt the dryness of salt-encrusted hair moving around her. 'I heard you. You called on the radio.' His hand released her. She jerked away a step, then stopped, her eyes held by his as she said stubbornly. 'They'll come.'

'No.' She managed to get a breath into her lungs when he stepped away. He walked over to his jeans. She saw him grimace as he touched the damp denim. 'It's standard procedure, calling. I knew no one would hear me.'

'But how——'

'Damn it! Don't you understand? Down here we're miles from the base, miles from everywhere. We were below the mountaintops, hemmed in. My transmission wouldn't have carried to anyone at all!'

She fumbled with the ties on the sleeping-bag as he struggled into the damp jeans. He couldn't be right, could he? She felt a horrified terror growing, said desperately, 'We're on the water. They'll start searching, won't they? Surely they know you're missing, and they'll start to search? They'll see us.'

She heard his zipper. Her eyes flew up, pleading for him to agree that they would be rescued, then got stuck watching as he did up the belt. She didn't know him. He had a family and she wasn't the kind of woman who had casual affairs, or any affairs. And how could she watch, her mind filling with—— How could she, when they were out here in the bloody bushes, and where were the damned rescuers?

'Is that better?' he asked, laughing.

She squeaked, 'What?' She had to get over this. Think about rescue. Think about anything but him. 'Is what better?'

'My jeans.' He stepped towards her.

She stood up, losing her balance and jerking straight, breathless. She jerked as he touched her cheek with a callused hand. Then she was still. This was a rough man, yet last night his touch had been as gentle as the fingers lying against her cheek now, as soft as the waves of his dark hair. 'Do you feel more comfortable now that I'm dressed?'

She swallowed. 'Yes. Yes, I do.'

'I want to thank you, Crystal.' She could feel the flush rising from her neck. He smiled a little, said, 'For getting me out of the ocean last night. For looking after me.'

She stared at his chin. There was a dark shadow, not a beard yet. 'I had to. I couldn't have survived a night alone out here.' Her eyes jerked to the trees and found another shadow that could be a bear.

'No, neither of us could have. Hypothermia's a killer.' He brushed back the tangle of her hair and anchored it behind her ear. His slight smile stilled and he said gently, 'As for the rest of last night, I——'

'No! Please.' His wife. He was going to say he was sorry, that he had a wife and—— She didn't care, didn't want to know. She really just wanted to get away from here, from him, and forget how his touch had gentled on her. If there were a child, it would be hers. He would never know. 'Please, can we just forget that it happened?' She stepped back, shook her hair and tried with her fingers to comb through the tangles.

'Forget?' She trembled at the heat in his eyes, the smile growing again as he said in a low voice, 'Last night is something I'm not likely to forget for a long time.'

She gasped, 'I—I've got to get out of here! I'm supposed to be working in Queen Charlotte City today.' Her mind grasped desperately for details. 'I've a nine o'clock appointment. I've got to be there. I can't—I've got to find my audit-bag.'

'That black briefcase thing?' He frowned. 'Forget it. It's gone.'

She jerked around. The water was still, a glassy expanse that went from here across to those hills. 'Gone? Did it sink? How deep?'

He sighed, exasperated. 'Look, I don't know if it sank or not. Probably not. It's in the Cessna and the damned plane floated off somewhere on the tide. I can't spot it. Right now, who the hell cares? It's our lives that matter.'

She was horrified! 'You think the plane is floating somewhere? Someone could find it? No! We've got to do something! That bag has files in it! It mustn't be found by anyone but me!' She couldn't believe that she was in this auditor's nightmare, her records lost and confidentiality compromised.

'Don't be an idiot!' His shout echoed around them and she could only stare. What kind of a man was this? Didn't he understand how serious this was?

'Only one thing matters.' His rigid voice grated and she stepped back, away from him. 'We have to survive. To do that, we have to walk out of here. No one is going to find us.'

She didn't believe he was serious. The rocks were sharp against the shore. She might climb along them, but they only went to—— Just there, and then they died into that tangle of thick green. 'Where?' she demanded. 'Where do you suggest we walk? There's nowhere to go. There's no path.'

'Path?' He laughed harshly and jerked his head towards the bushes. 'There. That's where we're going.'

'No! We've got to stay here where we can be seen. Not——' It would be full of bears in there, and other things she hadn't even thought of. Hadn't she heard of a girl being attacked by a mountain lion somewhere up north? 'Listen! I hear a plane!'

She ran out to the edge of the gravelly green, searching the skies. She could hear it, somewhere nearby. 'There it is, just coming over that hill. Hey! Hey, down here!' She waved her arms wildly in a big arc, shouting words without knowing what they were.

The floatplane was a small dot against the hill on the far side of the channel. It flew straight and level while she screamed at it. When it was gone only the sound remained. She didn't know there were tears on her face until Jesse came and brushed them away.

She screamed, 'Why didn't you try to signal him? You just stood there. Why—why wasn't he searching for us?'

'He was.' He ran his hands down along her arms, felt the trembling. His face was sombre, his eyes deep pools she could not read as he said, 'We've got to get you warmer.'

'Aren't they looking for us?' Why did she feel so drained? She mustn't let the tears get control. She wailed, 'Why aren't they looking for us, Jesse?'

She felt his fingers digging into her arms. 'They are. All the planes will be looking for us today.' His hands were warming her arms, slowly the trembling was stopping. He was watching her so intently that she knew she must be looking a terrible mess.

She whispered, 'Tell me what's going to happen.' She wished he would hold her close, and he seemed to hear the thought because his fingers curled around her upper arms and he drew her against his chest. He stood very still then, just holding her. 'Just take it easy, honey. Take some deep breaths and settle down.'

She sucked in a ragged lungful, then another. Slowly, the sounds of water lapping on rocks intruded. Then wind, the sound of a breeze rustling the dark green branches overhead.

'I'm sorry,' she said unsteadily. 'I'm sorry I screamed at you. I—I'm scared. I never—I'm really not an uncontrolled person. Not normally.'

He held her a little closer. 'Too controlled. I can see it, all that emotion inside you, trapped. Sometimes you have to let it out. If screaming at me helps, go ahead.'

'No. No, I——' Murray had said that she was just burying her needs and emotions, but it was not true. And this man—what was he doing, looking through her? 'I just want to know what's going to happen. Please tell me. If I know, I can handle it.' She trembled in his arms and hoped she was telling the truth.

'All right.' He released her slowly, taking her hand in a warm grip and leading her into the sunshine. 'Sit here. It's warmer in the sun. Now, listen carefully. Last night I should have reported in, closed my flight plan at Queen Charlotte City. When I didn't, people would have been worried, but not desperate. I might have landed somewhere to avoid weather and not been able to make radio contact. I might have had engine problems and set down on the water. In fact, that's what happened. We——'

'Set down?' Incredibly, she was laughing. The sun was on her and she was laughing aloud, and she was probably insane. 'You can't call that setting down, surely? Setting is a gentle motion, and——'

'It would have been,' he insisted. 'If everything had gone the way it should, last night would have been a minor inconvenience. We'd have landed, relatively smoothly, and I would have looked for the engine problem. If I couldn't fix it and take off again, we would have sat on the water, relatively warm and dry inside the Cessna.' He grimaced. 'I wouldn't have slept very well because I'd have had to keep making sure we didn't float into the shore, but you could have curled up in the sleeping-bag in the back seat and had a fairly good night.'

She shook her head. She would have been raging, impatient to get to work, angry at having the day messed up by one more disaster.

'Then,' he continued, his hand still holding hers, 'in the morning I would have waited to hear a plane flying overhead. I would have fired up the radio and called the pilot, arranged for a mechanic and another plane to get you to QC City. That would have been the end of it for you.'

She would have been a few hours late, but by now she might have been at the audit scene. Last night, making love with him in the sleeping-bag—that would never have happened. She would not have been pushed into the cold water, not have clung to the log for survival.

'Thank goodness for that log,' she breathed, knowing she could never have swum to shore from the plane.

'That bloody log was the cause of all our problems!' He released her hand and paced across the clearing, swinging back and glaring at her with his eyes on yesterday. 'I was just setting us down when I saw the damned thing! I hadn't much leeway, none at all, but I knew we were gone if we landed on it. It would have torn that Cessna to bits, and us with it! I tried to lift us over it, but I knew there wasn't much chance.'

'But we didn't hit it.' There had been no impact, only the sickening, bouncing, backward lurch, then the sinking, water everywhere.

'No, but the plane stalled.' He could see that she didn't understand and tried to explain, 'Without the engine she was a glider. I was flying her down, picking my landing spot. That's no real disaster, lots of places to land a seaplane in this country, but on a normal landing there's time to circle and watch for hazards on landing. We couldn't do that. We had to go right in, and by the time I pulled back for that log, we were just barely flying, almost on the water. When I pulled the nose up, the airspeed dropped and we stalled, stopped flying. I knew that could happen, but it was that or hit the log. The tail dropped and we hit the water. When a float plane lands that way, she almost always turns over, upside-down.'

Out on the water Crystal could see the shape of a boat powering into sight. She tensed, but he said gently, 'If you shout, you'll be exhausting yourself for nothing. He can't hear over the sound of his engines. There's no way he can see you. Look at our clothes. All neutral colours. Nothing to stand out from the trees.'

He was right. She couldn't see the people on the boat, so they surely could not see her.

'There's more, honey. Just listen.' He was determined to have his say and she shrugged, afraid to hear and knowing she would not like it. 'Rescue Co-ordination Centre will be on the job by now. All the emergency radio frequencies will have broadcast that we're missing. There won't be a boat or plane in the area with radio who doesn't know about us. They'll be watching for us. By now the rescue helicopters will be in the air, searching.'

This sounded better, more like what she would have expected. She sat up straighter, trying to see if there were any planes overhead. 'So they'll find us soon. We just have to wait and——'

'Honey, all they know is that we got as far as Kitkatla but didn't make it to Butedale. That restricts the search to a couple of hundred miles of wilderness coast and associated mountains and channels. The best we could hope for is that the pontoons from the plane will be sighted somewhere, sticking out of the water. That would restrict the search to fifty miles or so, the range of the tidal current. But the plane could have been damaged on the rocks and sunk, in which case it's two hundred fathoms underwater. These channels are deep!'

'But they'll search the shores,' she insisted, 'and we're on the shore. Stop being such a pessimist! You make everything sound so negative!'

'No, honey, I'm no pessimist.' He smiled and she felt suddenly very young, although she had reached her thirtieth birthday. 'But I'm no fool either. We're going to survive this, but not standing here. A boat could steam by a hundred feet off shore and you could be waving and screaming at it, and there's no way the people on board would see you. You saw what happened when that plane flew past. That's why we have to start walking, to save ourselves. Some planes disappear and are never found. We can't sit here, getting weaker, waiting for other people to rescue us. We've got to walk out.'

Walk out. He made it sound so simple, but she could see the trees, the bushes. She knew there was no path, no trail. 'Couldn't we make a raft?' She didn't know why he had not thought of this obvious solution. 'We could make a raft, then paddle out there and flag down a boat.'

'What are we going to cut down the trees with?' he asked gently. 'My jack-knife?'

She gave up, said wearily, 'I'm hungry.'

He dropped his arms. 'All right. So am I. That's one of the things we have to work on. I think we can find some late salmon-berries farther up the hill. There are other things we can eat, but berries are the easiest and the most palatable.'

'Up—into the bushes?' She couldn't do it. There was no way she could go walking through those trees, hemmed in, bait for the bears and the mountain lions. 'I'm not going. I'm staying here until someone comes.'

He sighed. 'Listen, honey, you've got to understand. We can't stay here.'

She jerked straighter, ignoring the jab of the rock on her behind. 'What about your emergency locator? Don't all planes have them?'

'Sure, but it's set off by inertia, and I don't think we hit the water hard enough to activate it. Face it, honey. If the locator had done its job, the rescue helicopters would be as thick as black flies. Speaking of black flies, we were lucky to come ashore here for our first night. It seems to be pretty bug-free.'

The first night? How many nights did he foresee? With bugs added to the rest of the horrors? She stared off over the water, determined not to cry again. Was that another boat? Yes, but the darned thing was too far away to see the people. But——

'Jesse, we could start a fire. They'd see the smoke, wouldn't they?'

'Maybe,' he agreed. 'Have you got any matches?'

'A lighter. I—no, it's in my bag. On the plane.'

'Mine is in my pocket, but it doesn't work. I think the salt water finished off the flint. I tried taking it out and scraping it, but it's had it.'

She bit her lip, looking around, searching for an idea. She was used to problems, but they always had solutions.

He said mildly, 'If you can come up with something I haven't thought of, I'd be grateful, but don't suggest I do a boy scout stunt with the twigs. This is the North Coast. It's been raining three days out of every five this last month, and there's no way you can get a piece of wood to ignite without matches or a lighter.'

Talking of matches and fires had reminded her of the cigarettes in her bag. She said bleakly, 'You wouldn't have a cigarette, would you?'

'No. Couldn't light it anyway. I guess you just quit smoking.' He turned away and started examining the rocks, as if he were looking for something.

She glared at his back. 'You could sound more sympathetic. Typical non-smoker. Virtuous and——'

'Don't lay that on me, honey.' He turned, grinning at her, the laughter that seemed a part of him surfacing again. 'I've done my own battle with that habit. If I quit, so can you. Today we've got worse problems than your wanting a cigarette.'

She said desperately, 'You just want to walk off into the bushes? Where are we going? Why?'

'To Butedale. It's a deserted cannery town down——'

'Deserted!' The man was crazy! 'You're taking me to a ghost town?'

He picked up a piece of white from the rocks. 'Styrofoam cup. We might find that handy.' Then he jumped up from the rocks on to the clearing. He stuffed the cup into the sleeping-bag cover, walked over to the sleeping-bag she had so carefully rolled earlier, caught the tie with one hand and pulled it open. She watched, unbelieving, as he rolled it out, unzipped and spread it on the grass. Did he think he was going to take her to bed again? Did he really have the nerve to think that she would be willing?

'There's a wharf there,' he said absently, carefully pulling the sleeping-bag into the sun. 'There used to be caretakers, too, but now I hear it's usually abandoned. No radio, which is too bad, but quite a few of the fishermen are in the habit of tying up there overnight, just passing through. They've got radios.' He nodded his satisfaction with the location of the bag, turned and grinned at her. 'It should dry there. Now, we'd better do something about our feet.'

'Our feet?'

'We've got to walk, and we need protection for our feet.' It was like something out of a Tarzan movie. He went over to his jacket, then he sat down and took his pocket knife to the thick sheepskin-lined leather.

'I found some old fishing net here,' he explained as he worked. 'I think I can use it as a twine and make a sort of a moccasin.'

She came closer, fascinated, watching him turn a length of sleeve into something that fitted his foot, then twisting holes into the sheepskin and fabric with his pocket knife.

'Could you get me that piece of fishing net?' He didn't look up, but gestured to the edge of the bank.

She picked it up and dragged it over to him, telling him, 'This is what I used to haul you out of the water last night.' She sat down cross-legged on the grass. Her slacks were already ruined and besides, this caveman stuff was crazily fascinating.

His fingers stilled. He looked up, those black eyes warm almost to brown as he said quietly, 'I wondered how you got me out.'

Had he? Last night, in the water, he had simply told her to get him ashore, then passed out. She smiled, remembering. 'I tied the fishing net around you, under your arms. I put the sleeping-bag around to protect you first. That's why it was a bit wet. Then I got up here and pulled.' His eyes met hers and she shrugged away what she saw in them. 'It took a while. I didn't hurt you, did I?'

'No.'

She bit her lip, wanting to look away, but something in his face would not let her. 'I was afraid I wouldn't be able to get you out.'

'You saved my life.'

The sun was beginning to work its way through the clouds. She looked away, said uneasily, 'I couldn't have if I hadn't come out of that plane. You did that, got me out.'

'Yes. I flew us into the water, so it seemed reasonable that I should pull you out of the plane. Part of the service, as it were.' She laughed, which he seemed to have wanted. His eyes warmed as he teased, 'I don't think this is what you paid for back in Prince Rupert, is it?'

Amazingly, she was giggling, unable to sober herself. 'Not exactly. Although you did warn me. You said you needed my name in case we crashed.'

'That was a joke.' He sounded angry. 'A stupid joke. I don't know why I said it. Something about the way you looked at me. You got my back up, I guess. I don't usually talk to customers that way.'

'Jesse——' The humour evaporated and she pleaded, 'Do we really have to walk out of here? Into those bushes?' He was silent, working on the moccasin. She swallowed. 'Look, I'm an auditor. I'm not really very much on bushes.'

'I know. You're a city girl, and you've never been this far from civilisation in your life.' She nodded, although he did not look up to see. He gripped one end of the moccasin between his knees and said casually, 'It's all right, honey. You'll be fine. If you can pull a six-foot man out of the water and up a cliff, you can walk out through those bushes.'

'It isn't muscles.' She shivered, her eyes glued to those trees. 'Last night there was a bear out there. I heard it.'

'Might have been.' He cut open a section of netting, then worked at it, freeing a lengthening string of green net. 'Could have been a beaver, too. Or a raccoon.'

'What about mountain lions?' she asked nervously.

He shook his head. 'Not so likely. I don't think you would have heard a cougar—those cats are pretty quiet. Probably never see one. A bear's most likely.'

'Thanks a lot,' she said sulkily, hearing her own voice and wishing she weren't foundering in such an emotional storm. From tears to laughter to sullenness. Where was her usual calm?

'What do you want me to tell you? Lies? That there aren't any animals out there? This country's full of wildlife.' He didn't look up. He was using the net as a rope to sew the edges of the makeshift footgear, frowning while he worked.

She swallowed, said raggedly, 'Listen, I'm sorry, but I can't do it. I can't spend hours walking through those bushes and—bears and cougars and—how far? How far is it?' Maybe she could do it for an hour, grit her teeth and walk.

He shrugged, considering. 'Ten or fifteen miles. I'm hoping we can do it in a couple of days.'

'Days?' Her breath drained from her lungs. She thought she would never get air in again, thinking of days in those bushes, shadows and wild things all around, waiting to pounce. 'Days? No! I can't—days? I can walk ten miles in two or three hours.'

'Not that kind of walking, honey.'

'Stop calling me honey! I'm not your honey! I——'
Oh, lord! She was screaming, her arms flailing. She was
going to pieces and she mustn't. 'I'm hungry,' she whispered. 'Can't we just find some food and stay here?'

He finished the first shoe, started working on the
second. 'I'll do footwear for you when I've finished
these, but first I'll go looking for some berries. We do
have to eat.' He looked up, his eyes sombre. 'Honey, we
can't stay here. There's nothing but salt water here.'

She hadn't thought about thirst until he said that, but
suddenly she was desperate for a drink. She wanted to
curl up and cry. This was too much. Yesterday had been
too much. It was time for it to end.

'Hey!' Fingers under her chin, lifting her face, dark
eyes penetrating hers. 'Snap out of it, honey.' His lips
pressed against the salty moisture on her cheeks. 'This
is not the time to give up. We survived last night. That
was the hard part. The cold didn't get us. We're here,
and we're still healthy. We'll find water, food, and we'll
walk out to Butedale.'

'I can't.'

He wouldn't listen. He was kissing away the tears. 'If
you can pull me out of that water alone, with just a
scrap piece of fishing net, you can surely walk to
Butedale. You're a fighter, not a quitter.'

She wished the trembling would stop. 'You don't
understand.' She closed her eyes and shuddered. 'What
if a bear comes out of those bushes? What if he comes
after us?'

He shrugged, then laughed and said, 'You're a pretty
resourceful lady. You'll think of something. Are you
really a tax auditor? You work for the government?'

'Yes.' She bit her lip, realising that he was amused.

'What were you going to do on the Charlottes?'

'Routine audits.' She wasn't about to tell him who. That was confidential. 'We do a lot of that, picking random taxpayers and sending a team out to check several in an area.'

'So this year you picked the islands.' He was grinning, the laughter rumbling deep in his chest. She remembered it from last night, but then the laughter had been warmer, just for her.

'What's so funny about that?' She was used to all the usual reactions to her occupation, but laughter? 'If the government never audited anyone, no one would pay taxes, and if no one paid——'

He was too close, the heat of him impossible on such a cold day. He brushed one tingling kiss on her lips, then retreated. 'I have a tax auditor at my mercy, the lady who's going to peruse my customers' books and tell all to the government. I should think about my goodwill, shouldn't I? If I come back without you, some of my customers might be very grateful.'

She jerked to her feet. 'You've got a foul sense of humour. Did anyone ever tell you that? You'd better watch yourself or I'll put you down for a tax review.'

That only made him laugh harder. 'Go ahead.' He was smiling, leaning closer again. 'I could use the opportunity to see you again after this, after last night I think we should pursue our relationship a little farther, back in civilisation.' His smile deepened suggestively. 'In a nice warm bed where——'

'Shut up! You're a horrible man! Someone will murder you one day! You—I'm going to look for some berries.' She was across the clearing in five steps, staring at the wall of trees. It wasn't just trees. Underneath the tall evergreens was a solid wall of bushes. She walked along them, away from him, trying to ignore his voice coming after her.

'Good idea, honey. But bring them back for me to check before you eat them. Mustn't have the tax auditor eating poison. And watch out for the bears.'

She gritted out, 'I'm Crystal. Could you please stop calling me honey?'

'That's what you taste like.' She stared ahead at the thick bushes. She would not look at him, not with that tone in his voice, the invitation, the memory of their naked bodies loving.

'I'll make you a deal,' he offered softly. 'You let me call you honey, and I'll protect you from the bears again tonight.'

'Again?' She found herself turning, staring at him, held by that magnetism that had been with her first sight of him. It wasn't that he looked like David. That had been the first thing, his hair and the back of his head. But this was something else, much more immediate than David's dimming memory.

'You were in my arms last night,' he reminded her softly. 'And the bears didn't get you, did they?'

She said hoarsely, 'It's not going to happen again. Not tonight.' She swallowed. 'Not any night.'

'Isn't it?'

It wasn't panic in her veins. It was desire, drugging her, drawing her towards the night and that single sleeping-bag that they would both need for warmth, for survival.

CHAPTER FIVE

SHE found some orange berries close by that looked like raspberries except for the colour. Salmon-berries, Jesse said, and they shared a handful. They were vaguely bitter, but the juice from them felt good as it trickled down her throat.

Then, when Jesse had finished the moccasins, they walked. She didn't think you would call it walking in any ordinary sense. It was more like a battle, pushing through impossibly dense branches. Jesse went ahead, using his pocket-knife and his arms, cutting when he had to, tearing through the bushes. She had to follow very closely, hold the branches aside as he passed them to her. Otherwise they would sweep in and slash at her, the thorns from the berry bushes cutting through the thin scraps of her blouse.

Half an hour after they started, he stopped abruptly. The silence grew around them. While they were moving she had been able to concentrate on fighting the dense growth. Stopping, she heard the silence, then little sounds.

'Let's go on,' she urged, trying not to feel the panic. If they had to stop, she wanted it to be in the open, without everything pressing in, life on all sides hiding heaven knew what kind of dangers.

'Not yet. Those bushes are tearing you up.' His finger traced the place where a thorny branch had torn into the ruined fabric of her blouse, the faint line of blood above her breast.

'I'm all right,' she insisted with a tinge of desperation. She shifted, trying to push past him. 'Let's go on. Moving keeps me warm.'

He had strapped the sleeping-bag and the remains of his damp jacket to his back, using the net to form a harness for his shoulders. Now he turned his back to her. 'Get my jacket out. The sleeves are gone, but it will be better for you to be covered and, climbing like this, you'll warm it quickly.'

She put it on. It was damp, cold...then warmer. 'Jesse, how far do you think we've gone?'

'Half a mile, maybe.' It had to be farther. He kept going faster than she could, then slowing for her, and they must have gone miles. 'I think we'd better slow down. This pace is exhausting us both.'

Panicked, she said, 'No!' His eyes narrowed and she realised that she was panting slightly. 'No, let's go on,' she insisted. 'I—I really want to get out of here as quickly as I can.'

'Alive,' he said softly. 'Honey, we're going to get out alive.' Then he said, *'Tú no hablas español?'* and she stared at him as if he was crazy.

'What? What?'

'I asked you if you speak Spanish.'

'Why?' She choked on a hysterical giggle. 'Do the natives here speak Spanish?'

'No, but I don't speak any native Indian tongues.' He grinned then and offered, 'But I do speak a little Spanish, and I could teach you.'

Astounded, she said, 'Why in the devil would I want to learn Spanish? I want to get out of here! That's all I want.'

He shrugged and said lightly, 'You might find it useful if you ever want to go to Mexico. I go every winter for a holiday. It's nice. Lots of sunshine, friendly people. But they speak Spanish.'

'You're crazy!'

'Maybe.' He turned and looked the way she supposed they were going. She kept losing her bearings and hoping he knew where they were. He said, 'We're going to slow down. We can't do this as a panic-stricken dash to safety. We're climbing as much as we're walking, doubling back when we find a barrier we can't climb. I begin to understand why it took the guy two weeks to walk seven miles to Kitimat.'

'Two... No!'

He settled the burden on his shoulders more comfortably. She stood up, desperate to move on. He said, 'It's hard to concentrate on Spanish verbs and worry about the bears at the same time.'

She looked at the trees behind him, then nodded abruptly. 'All right. Teach me Spanish, then, but can we *please* go on now?'

'*Sí,*' he agreed, grinning.

Maybe she would go to Mexico. It couldn't be any wilder than this, and he had the knack of teaching. By the time the sun set, she was calling the trees *los árboles* without thinking twice, and she hadn't thought of bears in an hour.

Jesse found a stream just at sunset. She collapsed on the sleeping-bag when he spread it, exhausted and oblivious to the bears. He started to tell her the words for sleeping and waking, and she closed her eyes and let his voice wash over her until sleep caught her.

She woke with the sun, his arms around her and her body stripped of clothing. He had undressed her. She remembered vaguely his voice telling her that she would be warmer in the bag without clothes to inhibit the

warmth between them. The night held no memories of
shared passion, only exhaustion and his warm arms.

The first night had been different, an insanity she
hoped his Lucy would understand, but he was being
faithful now, his arms impersonal, just for warmth. She
managed to dress before he woke, then wondered if he
only pretended to sleep to give her privacy. He was up
the instant she was dressed, then it was she who turned
away to avoid watching him walk across the clearing in
his briefs.

She was tired, sore, and the day passed in a painful
fog of muscles protesting their misuse as she followed
him up an endless green mountain that Jesse called *la
montaña*. They were nowhere near Butedale yet, but they
had found the black flies, and Jesse had no idea of the
Spanish word for them, although he thought he could
translate the little monsters he called *no-see-'ems*.

Dark came, the third night. She accepted the warmth
of the sleeping-bag, trying to sound amused as she said,
'I've learned more than Spanish today. I've learned that
black flies bite but don't hurt much, but that those mis-
erable little *no-see-'ems* bite like wolverines and itch like
mosquitoes.'

He laughed, and they scratched the bites, then slept
together with his arms around her for warmth, his hands
not touching.

She was not as tired as she had been the night before.
She twisted and itched and wished for a hamburger or
some peanuts. She knew she could hear the bears out
there. She wanted to wake him up when the sounds
stirred the wild, but she managed to contain her fear and
let him sleep. She tried very hard not to wish for his
hands to close on her, to caress as his lips sought the
places that made her lose control.

Finally, just before dawn, she became too exhausted for the fear to keep her awake. She slept and dreamed that there was a home under the trees, a man with Jesse's dark face coming towards her as she stood in the doorway waiting.

It was the next morning that they finally reached a point where they could follow the land without climbing. Then the going seemed easy, almost comfortable, and they were laughing like children enjoying a walk.

'Talk to me,' she urged.

'*Hablar?*' he teased. 'About what? The universe? The path of mankind? The crisis in the Middle East?'

'Are you kidding?' She put her hands on her hips and managed to look disapproving. Crazy, but the world seemed good with the going flat and easy and the green all around, the brilliant blue overhead. 'You know, if I ever get out of here, maybe I'll go camping sometimes. This isn't so bad.' She could just see the far shore of the water from their high lookout. There was a boat, far away, but she knew it was not for them and she hardly thought of it. She said gaily, 'I don't want to be depressed. I can hear the Middle East on the news. Tell me about this island.'

There were still bears out there, unseen but threatening. She listened to Jesse, letting his voice drown out the hazards, then became interested despite herself. There had been logging camps, canneries, people who had loved this island. There was lots of time for his talk, and he told her some of the native history as they walked.

Later, when he was silently concentrating on getting up a difficult hill, he got ahead of her. She looked up and he had turned a corner. She was alone, and immediately her nervousness returned. The shadows loomed everywhere and she jumped when a bush crackled.

'Jesse?' He didn't answer.

She rushed, stumbling to catch up again, but the toe of her moccasined foot caught on an underground root and she fell headlong. Then he was there, crouched beside her, his voice worried.

'You OK, honey? No, don't get up. Stay down for a second. How's your ankle?'

'It's OK.' She felt nauseated, not hurt. 'I just hit my knee on this root, but I'm fine.' His fingers probed the flesh around her knee.

She stared at him, felt dizziness overwhelm her and thought she saw a truth that had been hidden for the last couple of days. They were never going to get out of here. Frightened, she said, 'Jesse, I've got to get out of here. I've got to get back to work!'

He was so close, crouched inches in front of her, his knees thrust out, bracketing her body. He leaned closer, balancing with one hand dropped to the ground.

He said, 'I think it's time you thought about something other than your job.'

She watched his head swaying on a wave of dizziness, then she studied the line of the creases around his eyes when things stilled again. She mumbled, 'Murray's always telling me that.'

'Who's Murray?' She blinked at the tension in his voice. His free hand caught her chin, tipped her head so that her eyes could not drop away from his, and he repeated insistently, 'Who is he?'

She could see his frown starting and she said quickly, 'He's a friend.' What was it to him? He was the one who was married. Irritated and nervous about the way her head kept spinning, she said, 'What about Lucy? Shouldn't you think about Lucy?'

'Lucy?' Startled, his hand jerked from her face, pushed back through his dark hair. The wilderness had taken its toll on those soft, black curls, yet she still wanted to touch his hair, twist her fingers through it.

'Lucy,' she insisted. What kind of a marriage did he have? 'Isn't it time you remembered her?'

'I haven't forgotten Lucy.' He grinned then, but she thought he looked sober under the smile. 'She's a hard lady to forget, but I'm damned if I can see what she has to do with this.' His knees shifted away from her as he rocked back on to his heels. 'How in the hell do you— do you know Lucy?'

'No.' She had wondered what kind of woman he would marry, had almost asked him once. It was hard to remember that he was married. 'What does she look like?'

'She—what the hell is this? Are you sure you're feeling all right? Did you hit your head when you fell?'

'I'm fine. I just asked——'

'All right.' She didn't realise how her voice had risen until he touched her, as if gentling a wild animal. 'Take it easy, honey. It's just that I thought auditors were logical types, and this doesn't make much sense. Anyway, Lucy—well, she's—I guess about your height. She's a redhead, too. She—— '

'I'm not a redhead!' Was that why he kept looking at her like that, his eyes touching, caressing? Because of the hair? The height?

'Well, auburn, then. Whatever you call it. Lucy keeps her hair short. She says it's easier when she goes sailing.' His voice was warm. You could tell he was talking about someone he cared for. 'She's—— ' He spread his hands, seeming to find words inadequate. 'She's kind of a wild thing. You wouldn't expect someone like her to be an accountant.'

She winced. That was a direct hit. Maybe his wife was more to his taste than Crystal Selwyn. Well, of course she was. He had married her. But he didn't have to contrast them, as if Crystal's profession made her sterile and dull beside the woman he had married.

He bent over her. 'Are you sure you're OK? Honey, you look terrible.'

'Don't touch me!' She jerked away from his hand. 'I—how can you do this?' She stumbled, trying to rise, but the knee was unexpectedly wobbly.

He caught her in his arms and pulled her close, trapping her against his chest, his hands going to her hair, fingers slipping under, probing her scalp.

'What are you doing? Let me go!' She felt dizzy from his nearness. She closed her eyes tightly, wincing, trying to bring in a clear picture of the short-haired Lucy he belonged to.

'That hurts, doesn't it?' He had the sound of someone who had been proved right after an energetic argument. 'I know you must have hit your head. Now, just take it easy.'

'I'm not——'

'Shh!' He was still, perfectly quiet. She froze, pressed against him, listening desperately for the sound he had heard. She had known the bears would come eventually.

'You wait here,' he said finally, his voice low. 'I'll——'

'No! I'll come with you! You're not leaving me alone with the bears!'

'Easy.' His hands soothed as his voice did.

'Stop treating me like an invalid! I'm not staying here alone with a bear out there! I won't—stop laughing at me!'

'Crystal—honey, I swear that there's no bear out there.' He raised his hand like a boy scout making a vow. 'I haven't seen any fresh bear sign all day. And——'

'I heard him last night!'

'You heard something,' he agreed. 'But I don't think it was a bear this time. I saw old tracks this morning, but they're at least two weeks old.'

She didn't believe he could look at a track and know its age, yet he had the air of a man who told the truth, regardless of the consequences.

Would he tell Lucy the truth when he got back home?

His hand was on her forehead, then he forced her down on the dirt bank behind her. 'Stay here while I find a place for us to set up camp.' Her lips parted and he bent over her, giving her a hard, quick kiss. 'Shut up,' he said softly. 'Be quiet and stay put.'

Then he left her alone. The shadows were all around, but it was no use her moving. If the bears were going to get her, she could not stop them. She certainly could not run with her knee throbbing and the bushes thick all around.

When he came back he was smiling. 'I found it. It's not far, and believe it or not there's almost a path. I guess it's a game trail. Do you think you can walk if I put my arm around you?'

It wasn't too hard, and it seemed natural to rest against him, to feel him holding her safely. She kept her eyes on her feet, and tried to make the knee work, then gave up and let Jesse take the weight off it.

Jesse. She shivered, feeling the warmth surging up. In all her life, she could not remember wanting a man like this, even David, but these nights were getting to her. God, but the man was magnetic! Or was it the isolation, the sense of danger?

She had to remember Lucy. She mumbled, 'Are you going to tell her? Are you, Jesse?'

'Here, stop trying to put your weight on that leg.' He held her a little tighter, lifted slightly to avoid a buried root. He seemed to be ignoring most of the things she said, as if she were talking nonsense. He said, 'I'd carry you, but the path is pretty uneven. Tell who?'

'Lucy.' She gasped as a shaft of pain shot up her leg. 'I think it's—oh!'

He swung her into his arms then, striding quickly out into a small clearing under the trees, lying her down carefully, then shedding the gear from his back. 'I'm going to spread out this bag. I want you to sit on it, then take your trousers off so I can look at your knee. And I want to have a closer look at your head. You must have really cracked it one when you fell.' He had the sleeping-bag spread out. He turned back purposefully towards her.

'I can move myself.' She scurried across to the bag, glad to leave the six-legged thing she could see crawling on the ground. It wasn't a spider, so what was it? 'My knee's OK. I'm OK. Do you think there will be *no-see-'ems* here?'

'I hope not.' He shrugged and walked away to the creek. It was a thin stream of water, twisting around the rocky ground, through the dense trees. His words were tossed back casually. 'Honey, take those things off, or I'll take them off.'

She asked, 'Does this stream go down to the ocean?' and he ignored her as if it were a silly question.

He meant it about taking her trousers off. Damned macho northerners! A city man wouldn't have the nerve to make a threat like that to her. She winced as she twisted to undo the zipper at her waist. It was more than she needed to have him touching her leg, examining the knee. To have his hands at her waist, undoing the zipper—— She wasn't sure if she could hide the trembling from his nearness if he did that. It was getting worse every day, and she was terribly afraid she might ask him to love her when dark came again.

When he finally touched the flesh at her knee, the pain was too severe for her to do anything but cry out. He winced at her pain, but his hands were steady, probing gently but firmly.

'I don't think it's anything drastic, honey. But it is swollen, and you're going to have to stay off it for a while.' He looked up, over her head and towards the stream. 'We'll rest here tomorrow. I'll work on collecting some food for us while you rest. Then we'll go on the next day. If your knee is better.'

From somewhere came a beating sound, growing louder, pounding through the trees. 'Helicopter,' said Jesse, looking up as though he could see through the trees. 'It's a big one. Sikorsky, probably the Air-Sea Rescue chopper.'

She sat up, straining to rise. 'We should——'

'No. It's too high. He can't see us. People are almost impossible to spot.' How many times had he told her that? 'He's surveying the route I would have taken, looking for signs of the Cessna. Something metallic, a flare sent up. Anything that stands out.'

Then the sound was gone and there was only the wild, and Jesse. She stared at him and repeated, 'Are you going to tell Lucy?'

He twisted back to her, looking down on her as she lay spread out on the sleeping-bag. She thought she must look a mess, torn and tattered, swollen knee and tangled hair.

'Tell her what?' he asked patiently.

'About me,' she whispered. 'Will you tell her that we made love that first night?'

He was silent a long time, then he said uncomfortably, 'I don't know. I—yeah, I suppose I probably will. Or she'll know somehow, when I tell her about the crash.' He shrugged, his voice defensive. 'I wouldn't tell just anyone, but she is kind of special.'

'I should think so.' Crystal tried to sound outraged, but her voice was just a whisper.

'They'll have me to dinner when I get back,' he explained. 'And they are my best friends.' He pushed his hands through his hair. 'I don't know how we got on to this. You're delirious, I think, but—well, I wouldn't want you to think I'm the kind of man who brags about his conquests. I—but I doubt if I could hide it from Lucy. Sometimes I think the woman's psychic. It's a good thing Max doesn't try to play around on her, because he'd never make it.'

'Max?' Maybe she had hit her head, but he was not making sense. 'Who's Max?'

Exasperated, he said, 'You're the one who brought up Lucy. Don't you know who Max is?'

'No, you brought her up.' She turned away, pulling one side of the sleeping-bag across to cover her bare legs. She couldn't put the trousers back on. It simply hurt too much.

'I am? I didn't——' He stopped abruptly, then said, 'Sorry. I forgot about your head. Let me take a look.' He knelt beside her, bending over her, his hands approaching her head.

'No!' She jerked away. 'There's nothing wrong with my head! I—it was you who phoned Lucy. You said sorry about dinner, and you wouldn't be home tonight. Please look after the girls for me. Stop poking through my hair!'

'All right.' He smoothed her hair, his hand unobtrusively feeling for evidence of fever. 'Why don't you try to get some sleep? I'll bring you a drink, then you can sleep.'

Her angry eyes met his and could read nothing in them. 'What about the girls?'

'They'll be OK. Lucy's looking after them,' he explained patiently.

'Lucy's not your wife?'

'No. She's my accountant. She's Max's wife.' He spoke slowly, as if explaining to a child.

'So where's your wife?' She might as well find out what the score was. Had she helped a man cheat on his wife? Or not?

'Oh, for heaven's sake!' he exploded in exasperation. 'Look, let me go and get you some water. Then I can tell you my history, if you really want to know.'

She shook her head, feeling doggedly stubborn about this. 'I want to know about your wife.'

'I don't have one.' He was shouting. Her mouth parted to protest and he pressed his fingers to her lips, his voice dropping. 'I don't know what it is about you, honey. I'm really not the kind of man who shouts and bullies, but——' He laughed. 'You do know how to upset my equilibrium. Now, please hush and let me get the water. I know you don't think so, but you've got a touch of fever.'

He was gone, returning a moment later with their single Styrofoam cup filled with water. He held it for her to drink, then bunched up the cover from the sleeping-bag as a pillow for her head and pushed her down gently on the bag. 'Sleep now, honey. You really do need it.'

'How did you get the girls?' She was weakening. It really felt good to close her eyes. 'If you don't have a wife, how did you get the girls?'

She started to shiver despite the bag around her. Then he was beside her, drawing her into his arms, saying, 'Look, you've got to get warm somehow. Come here.'

If there was no wife, there was no reason not to let him draw her close. Even if his hands did touch, caress.

She didn't have affairs, but this one was already started, and somewhere in the swimming recesses of her mind she knew that his child would be a good thing for her. She wanted to be a mother again.

'What about the girls?' she mumbled, her voice protesting while her body found the place where she fit best against him.

He circled her back with his warm arm and said, 'I got Siam from a litter my brother had.'

'What?' She could not have heard right. 'A litter?'

'Tabby was a stray.'

'A stray?' she repeated dully.

He laughed, the chuckle vibrating through her. 'Honey, you're repeating everything I say. Yes, she was a stray. I opened my door one morning and there she was.'

She lay still in his arms, taking it in. He was right. Her mind was fuzzy, but——

'The girls are cats?'

'Of course they're cats.' He pulled the covers over himself, twisting to bring her alongside his whole body. 'Is that comfortable? How about your knee?'

She snuggled closer. The bears would never come with him awake. He would stare at them with those black eyes and frighten them away. 'What did you imagine my girls were?' he asked, the question following her into her foggy dream.

She shifted against him, felt the warm security of Jesse against her, and asked drowsily, 'Are you going to make love to me tonight?'

Through the fabric of his jeans she could feel his body respond to her suggestion, but he whispered unsteadily. 'Not tonight, honey. Tonight you're not yourself. You're going to sleep.'

That was the last thing she heard before the dreams took over. When she woke, the sky was dimly grey, the world black and white, no longer coloured. She closed her eyes again, turning, her hand reaching for Jesse.

She was alone. She might be alone in the world for all she knew. She was lying in a little clearing, the sleeping-bag spread out on a mat of small twigs and un-identifiable soft, dry pieces of matter. She had a terrible headache.

She jerked around when she heard a twig break, her hand going to her throbbing head as she stared at nothing. Shadows. Formless monsters in the trees.

Where was Jesse?

A movement. Something!

There! A small mound of reddish-brown scampered around the bottom of a tree, pausing motionless for an instant of eternity to stare at her, then circling the trunk, tiny legs scurrying as he went.

A squirrel! She giggled, relieved that Jesse was not here to see her idiocy. Crystal Selwyn, the cool ac-countant, the fearless tax auditor, terrified of a squirrel.

She flexed her knee carefully. It seemed better now, and her head wasn't too bad if she kept it still. She had thought it was only a couple of hours since Jesse had cradled her in his arms, soothing her to sleep, but the sky was brightening with dawn now.

Had she dreamed that conversation about Lucy and the girls? The girls were cats, the wife an accountant— but not his wife. His image was vivid, the feel of his fingers brushing her cheek, his eyes laughing, probing gently. She shivered as the sun's rays found her. There was no warmth in the sun, only in the night, in Jesse's nearness and the heat it brought.

What if they had an affair, continuing what they had started? She tried to think of later, afterwards, but her only reality was here, Jesse and the bushes. Later, if there was a later, it would be another world. And if there was a child it would be hers. She pushed the sleeping-bag away, knowing it was what she wanted. Someone to share her life when this was over. She couldn't go back to that apartment, back to the emptiness she had not realised was hers.

She sat up and shook it off, the funny, dreaming thoughts that seemed to come with the trees and the cool air. Overhead, she could see a massive shadow. She stared up and knew that it must be a bald eagle, giant and awesome, surveying his domain.

She heard the little sounds the forest made. She was growing used to most of them. Sometimes she forgot the threat of bears and mountain lions. She listened carefully, but there was no sound that would be Jesse returning.

She stripped her clothes off and crouched down in the hollow where the stream made a pool of cool, clean water, trying to ignore the icy cold of the mountain stream.

As she washed without soap, she was constantly aware of a delicious feeling of dread. Any minute Jesse would step out of the trees and see her here, crouched down, naked, her hair wet and curling over her shoulders. He would come to her and his eyes would be deep, the black seeming to have colour, and he would touch her very softly.

No! It was daytime. She might let it happen in the night, with darkness and mystery around, but not now, with the sun rising over them.

She washed and drank deeply of the clear water where it poured over the rocks above the pool. Then she combed her hair with her fingers, hoping the sun would dry it quickly. It was amazing how cold it was in the nights up north, how even the mornings felt like winter.

Jesse did not return until just after she was dressed again. She had thought she would hear him; but when she finished buttoning her blouse she looked up and he was there, standing at the edge of the clearing.

He must have washed too, before she woke. His hair was messy, but shining in the sunlight, the salt coating gone. He was holding what looked like a plastic ice-cream bucket in one hand. He smiled as their eyes met and she realised that his smile was an answer to hers.

'You look like Davy Crockett,' she said, taking in the flannel shirt, that seemed to have crossed the continent, the jeans and moccasins.

'Except for the ice-cream bucket.' He held the yellow plastic up for her to see. 'My find for the day. Someone must have thrown it overboard as garbage. Normally I'd curse them for littering the wilderness, but when I went down to the shore and found it this morning, I thought I'd struck gold.'

He came towards her and for a moment she thought he would bend and kiss her lips. He stopped just short of touching, crouched down, showing her the contents of the bucket.

'Berries?' They were red and round and shiny, mercifully unlike the bitter salmon-berries. 'Are they edible?'

'Very.' He popped one into his mouth. 'Red huckleberries. Have some.' He held one out and she opened her mouth, her tongue touching his fingers as she took it. She felt breathless from that small contact, a wild desire to taste him all over.

'They're sweet.' She grinned. '*Bayas*. Is that right?'

'That's right. Have some more *bayas*.' He filled her hand and she gave herself up to enjoying them, stuffing a generous mouthful in, luxuriating in the taste and the feeling of plenty.

'Wonderful,' she managed around her filled mouth.

He popped a small handful into his mouth, promised, 'When we get out of here, I'll take you out for a real dinner. Whatever you want.'

An eternity ago, back in Prince Rupert, she had thought he might ask her to dinner. 'Nothing could taste better than this,' she insisted, grabbing another handful. 'I was so hungry!'

'They're good,' he agreed easily, settling his long legs more comfortably as he sat beside her. 'A bit wormy, but at least not overripe.'

She choked, swallowed because it was too late not to. 'Did you say—wormy? You mean worms?'

He said easily, 'Don't worry. They won't hurt you. Huckleberries almost always have worms in them. Little white worms. They don't——'

'Stop!' She swallowed convulsively. 'You—why did you feed me wormy berries?'

'Honey, you've got to eat, and this is what's on the menu. I could go down to the water and get you some mussels, and we could have them raw, or——'

'No!' Something was caught in her throat. A worm, she supposed. 'I need a drink of water.' She rushed to the stream, got herself soaked trying to scoop up water quickly with her hands. Her throat still felt funny. 'Can't we—— Isn't there a way to get rid of the worms?'

'Sure. Soak them for eight hours or so in water. I thought we'd pick some more before we start out and soak them in this bucket while we're going. But I figured for now—I don't know about you, but I couldn't wait eight hours to eat.'

She came back slowly, watching him fold the sleeping-bag and stuff it into its bag. 'Have some more,' he suggested, his voice neutral.

She shook her head, but he couldn't see. 'No—I——' She was terribly hungry, and they looked good. They had tasted good. She bit her lip, wondering if the salmon-berries had worms too, watching as he reached a hand and casually put a few more of the berries into his mouth. She picked up one. It felt clean and smooth. She couldn't see any worms. She started to bring it closer, to examine it, then abruptly closed her eyes and ate it, quickly.

'I found you a walking-stick,' he told her. 'I thought we could go on slowly today, if you figure you can walk on that leg? I was going to get you to stay in bed—or in bag, I guess I should say. But you're up and you look much better. How about it?'

'All right.' She stared at his back as he went to the stream and filled the ice-cream bucket half-full with water. She remembered how his body had stirred against her last night, and wondered how he could seem so impersonal this morning. 'Jesse, why did you tell me about the worms? You could have said nothing, and I'd have been able to eat the berries without knowing.'

'Is that what you want?' he asked harshly, turning back swiftly, faint anger in the way his lips turned down. 'Do you want me to protect you from the realities, to pretend the world is sugar-coated?'

David had done that. And she had fought it, hated it.

'Ready?' he asked, waiting, the water in one hand and his pocket-knife in the other, ready to clear the way for her. 'I think there's a game trail all along the side of this mountain. We'll get a couple of miles out of it.' He stared at her for a second, then asked again, 'Ready?'

'Yes.' She had everything. The walking-stick. The remains of his jacket covering her tattered blouse. The covering he had made for her feet. She started walking and he turned away from her, leading the way.

'Thanks for the stick,' she offered, but he didn't answer. Saving his breath, she supposed. She looked down at her legs, the dark stain of some kind of sap on her trousers, the right leg torn from something she could not remember. 'I must look a sight. It's too bad you don't have a camera. You could take a picture and I could take it back with me. They'd get a real charge out of this at work.'

He laughed then, finally, and she relaxed. It was all right. If Jesse was smiling, she thought she could handle anything. He said lightly, 'Picture of a tax auditor working in the field?'

'That's me,' she agreed gaily. 'I'm a good auditor. I'll go to any lengths to get my man.'

She didn't realise he had stopped. She was looking down, laughing, not heeding the words she was saying. Then he stopped and she walked into him, jarring him and sending water from the bucket splashing over both of them.

'Oh! I'm sorry! I——'

The smile was still in his eyes, fading. His lips were more like a frown, then coming closer. His hands were full. He was not holding or touching her. She could have drawn back, but she didn't. She waited for his lips, firm and cool, moulding the softness of hers.

His face, close and lit by the sun, was shadowed heavily by the growth of his beard. He looked like a dangerous man, but she was not afraid. If he had asked her then, in that instant, she would have been his, under the sun, in the wild.

'Did you?' he asked huskily, the black eyes holding her hazel ones.

She shook her head slightly, confused. 'Did I what?'

'Did you get your man?' He dropped the knife so that his hand could brush back the hair. 'Do you have a man, honey?'

She blinked, wishing there did not have to be questions. This was a world apart. She wanted it separate, to go back clean and . . . and forget whatever happened here.

'Is there a man?' He frowned, his voice dropping to a low growl. 'If I kiss you——'

The words were halted as his hand possessed the back of her head, fingers threading through her hair, bringing her close to his lips again. His lips possessed her, tongue probing to find the tender places that would strip her of breath, teeth taking her upper lip in a gentle victory that left her breathless.

She wasn't aware of letting the walking-stick go, only that her hands were free, slipping up around his shoulders, drawing herself closer, her breasts straining against him through the barrier of the thick jacket she wore.

She was still clinging when he drew away, her arms linked around his neck, her ears not really taking in what he said, so that he had to repeat it, a low voice as his lips came to her again.

'If I kiss you like this, am I stepping on anyone's territory?'

'No,' she whispered. 'No. I don't want anyone. Never again.'

His eyes narrowed, then seemed to blaze with some fire, as if she had challenged something in him. His fingers curled in her hair, bringing her close again. 'You don't want anyone?' he taunted softly, his lips nibbling the side of her mouth, head ducking down for his mouth to find the tender underside of her jaw. 'What about now?' he whispered as his hand left her hair, slid along the side of her neck, not quite tickling, moving softly.

The soft pressure of his fingers against her breast was exquisite agony. She ached for more, her body turning to give him access to the buttons that made a barrier. He fumbled, his fingers oddly awkward, then his hand possessed the warm curve of her woman's breast. She felt his breath go short as her own head fell back, inviting his lips to her throat.

'What about now?' he growled again, his lips seeking down, tongue exploring the soft swellings. 'Do you want . . . now?'

Yes. She did not know if she said it, or if it was only in her mind. Her lips parted and he possessed them before the sound could escape. Then the roaring in her ears grew until she felt him stiffen.

Everything stilled and he lifted his head, listening, searching their small piece of the sky through the branches.

'Helicopter?' she breathed. He nodded, still looking upwards. The sound grew, then faded, and he relaxed finally, his eyes dropping.

Still safe in his arms, she whispered, 'What can you tell from listening?'

'Guesswork.' He smiled ruefully. 'That was a smaller chopper, one of the local charter companies, I imagine. Everyone will be looking. He didn't see anything to make him slow down.' He looked down at her. 'Crystal——' His voice was low, filled with some emotion. His hand lifted, did not quite touch her cheek. She saw him swallow. 'You know, I——' He closed his eyes. She felt a shudder go through him, then he pulled away from her.

She pulled her arms back. He looked past her, back the way they had come, his eyes intent on something. She was abruptly aware of her blouse hanging open. She quickly fastened her buttons while he was not looking, then she brushed her hair back, combing it with her fingers, bending to the task and escaping his eyes.

Finally, it was she who broke the silence, saying tightly, 'Don't you think we should go on?'

'Yes,' he agreed tonelessly. Then he turned away and the journey resumed.

CHAPTER SIX

THEY walked steadily, the ground kind to them until late afternoon. Then, abruptly, they came upon a deep gully directly in their path.

Jesse stopped. Crystal came to his side, staring down at the void. They would never be able to cross it. They might go up, but—— Her eyes followed the fissure along the slope of the hill. Steeper and steeper, the deep gash disappearing into the trees—to go up and around would be for ever, all the way to the heavens. He set down the bucket. 'That's it for to——' His words dropped off to nothing and she saw his eyes narrow, intent on something across the ravine. Alarmed, she tried to follow his gaze.

'What is it?' she whispered.

His fingers closed over her wrist, commanding silence. Across the gully a black shadow moved, just another shadow in the thick growth. Then, at the edge of the rocks, the form stilled. Watching, she saw it rise up on hind legs and face them.

A bear. A black bear. The air stirred Crystal's hair lightly, carrying her scent towards the bear. He was so close, separated only by that gully. He stared at her through lazy eyes as his head swung slowly from side to side. His blunt-tipped nose probed the scents on the air. Fascinated, Crystal fancied that the bear blinked as it met her gaze.

The silence stretched endlessly. Crystal forgot to breathe. Then, abruptly, the sleek, black animal sank down on to four legs, head still cocked towards them.

It was then that she realised she felt no feeling of threat; although surely on four legs the bear could traverse the ravine between them?

He was moving, going where? His hunched black body became a ball, rolling slowly away. Then he was gone into the trees, moving silently downhill and away from them, disappearing quickly yet without haste.

She felt her breath return, felt Jesse's hand drop from her arm. 'I thought he'd make more noise,' she said, her voice out of place among the trees. Jesse shook his head silently, as if loath to disturb the spell. Crystal swallowed, watching the trees where the bear had gone. 'He was beautiful.'

Jesse let the sleeping-bag slip to the ground. He turned and smiled at her, said softly, 'I thought it was time you started to see the beauty.'

Bears could be dangerous. She knew that, yet she had felt no fear of that black animal. He had seen them and smelled them, then gone his way, as if acknowledging that they were all creatures sharing the forest.

She pushed back her hair. 'Right now——' Her voice was a little unsteady, but she continued. 'I—I know I should be back at work, doing something about my audit-bag, those files and the computer. I have to file a—I feel as if I could stay out here for ever.' Her eyes went to his, found a quiet understanding there. 'Jesse, do you—do you do this kind of thing a lot?'

'Three or four times a year.' He grinned then, his laughter bringing her smile. 'Not quite like this. Usually I try to keep the plane intact. I land in some protected lagoon, or get one of the other fellows to drop me off for a weekend. I bring a few more supplies.'

'Like what?' She looked at the things he had dropped to the ground and smiled. 'Don't we have everything we need? A bucket half-full of berries, a cracked Styrofoam cup, and a sleeping-bag?'

'Yeah. Next time I guess I'll pack less.' She saw the deep lines of his smile and felt warmed, content. He said, 'I won't bother with the matches, the pot to cook in, the radio.'

She squeaked, 'Radio? What do you do out here? Listen to pop music?'

'Not that kind of radio, honey. A portable transceiver, to contact any of the fellows who might be flying over, or—well, if they came to pick me up and I'd broken a leg or something, couldn't get to the rendezvous, I could call at the time and get help.'

'It would be different if I was alone,' she told him suddenly, thinking of Jesse out here by himself. He would be quietly enjoying himself, capable and competent in this wilderness. She remembered the bear and knew she would have been afraid if Jesse had not been there. 'I wouldn't be seeing the beauty then. I would be huddled somewhere, terrified.'

He spread out the sleeping-bag, said mildly, 'I doubt it. You wouldn't give up that easily.' He was crouched over the bag, knees thrust out. He looked up, his eyes deep. 'Sit down now and rest that leg while I see how our berries are doing.'

She accepted the softness of the sleeping-bag, slipping off the moccasins and enjoying the warmth that lingered from the exertion of their walk. 'You're wrong, though. I froze in that plane. And—there was a time when I just gave up.'

She didn't know why she wanted to tell him, but he was watching, waiting, and she said slowly, 'My husband died five years ago. And my son. After that—for a long time, I didn't care.'

She watched him draining the water from the berries before he turned and brought them to her. She found herself smiling a secret smile. Crazy that this wilderness could be enjoyable. He crouched down and they ate their feast silently.

'What happened?' he asked softly.

'It was an accident. A car accident.' His hand was dark against the bucket as he reached for another handful of the berries. She stared at it, remembering David's hand gripping the steering wheel in a hard moment of panic. 'I was in the car, too, but I wasn't hurt the way they were. I wasn't badly hurt, but emotionally I—it seemed like for ever, but I guess it was about six months or a year. Then, slowly... Murray helped. My mother and Murray.'

'Murray again? Your friend?' He touched the place at the back of her arm where the scar was still faint, seemed to know this was her legacy from the accident.

'My mother made me go to a counsellor.' She smiled then. 'That was Murray. I don't know what kind of psychology he practises. He just bullied me into getting myself together. I—After a while it got easier. I got a job and stopped going to counselling sessions.'

He picked up her hand, his fingers toying with hers. He said softly, 'Life began to seem worth living again?' She nodded mutely. She never talked about this. It was part of the other Crystal, the girl who dreamed dreams and thought there were happy endings. His fingers isolated her empty ring finger. 'You don't wear his wedding ring?'

She curled her fingers, slipping the ring finger free. 'I did. For a long time. Murray said I was clinging to the past.' Murray was always saying things like that, telling her to go out and get involved again.

'He sounds like a good friend.'

'He is.' He was her mainstay, the brother she had never had. 'I stopped wearing the ring a year ago.' It had been the anniversary of the accident, and she had known it was time to let it go. 'They're gone,' she said simply.

'What was his name?' His voice was rough, as if her loss was his.

'Johnny,' she said, then realised that he had meant her husband. 'David. My husband's name was David.'

He had her hand again and she let her fingers cling to his. Just for now, for a few minutes in the wilderness. Later she would stand alone again.

'Johnny——' She blinked and said, 'He was seven.'

He said softly, 'Honey, I'm sorry,' and that almost started the tears flowing.

She shook her untidy curls, blinking the moisture away. Her voice was unsteady as she begged, 'Jesse, please—I don't want to cry.'

'All right.' What made this man so understanding? He shifted towards her, said casually, 'Move over a little and let me have some of that sleeping-bag.' She felt his thigh pressing on hers. 'And tell me about your job.'

'Really?' She giggled, looking at his unshaven face, the dark tan that told anyone he was an outdoors man. 'It's not most people's favourite topic.'

'You like it, though?' She nodded and he said, 'So tell me why.'

'I don't know.' No one had ever asked that, and she was at a loss to explain. 'Everyone thinks it's like police work, trying to catch people. Actually, most people aren't trying to cheat on their taxes.'

'They're law-abiding citizens?' He made that sound reasonable, until he added, 'Like me. I go out of my way to pay my taxes.'

She laughed with him, scolded, 'You're crazy. But I bet Lucy works out ways for you to avoid taxes.'

He shook his head vigorously. 'You're not going to get me to incriminate my accountant. If she does, I'll never tell.'

'Tax avoidance is legal—using the legal loopholes. It's tax evasion that's against the law. Do you really want to hear this?'

'Yes, if it makes you smile.'

He traced the curve of her lips with a long finger. His light touch drained her smile away, leaving the muscles slack. Her tongue slipped out to wet the sudden dryness, and she felt panic without knowing why.

She said desperately, 'You know, what we should talk about is internal control. The system in your office looks OK, but you should do something about your tangible assets.'

His lips twitched. She wished he would be serious. His laughter unbalanced her insides in a way she could not handle at this moment, but he was doing it again, that warmth in his eyes as he said in a low voice, 'Here I am whispering sweet nothings to you, and you're telling me to secure my tangible assets.'

She swallowed and Jesse watched, enjoying it. He loved teasing her gently, seeing her flush at his words. Surely there was no other woman in the world who could look so appealing after five days of being dragged through the bush?

He saw the flush rising in her cheeks. Was she remembering the night that haunted him? He remembered how her body had felt under his, wondered how much of his memories were fantasy, how much real. One certainty—she had been his, in his arms and against his soul as he could never remember another woman being. Four nights ago, but he was hungering as if it had been for ever. If he touched her now, made her his again, would it be as it had before? This woman, her warm skin heating him, sending fire through all the frozen places.

She said, 'I'm serious,' and for a second she managed to look like an accountant, an auditor. He watched her lips move. Would the auditor disappear if he touched them with his?

'I'm serious, Jesse,' She was frowning, as if she felt he were not attending to her warning. 'Your employees could easily be ripping you off for fuel. You should be costing your fuel, matching every litre to your charters by plane and trip. There's no good control at your pumps and——'

He touched her lips with his fingers. Her words drained away and he could feel his heart hammering through his whole body. It was his voice that broke the long seconds of silence, husky from her nearness. 'Is that what you were doing down on the wharfs while you were waiting for your flight? Thinking about my control system?'

She seemed to have trouble talking. He brought his lips closer, brushed gently against her mouth, his heart wild as her voice lost its steady coolness. 'What should I have been thinking?' She added defensively, 'I was killing time.'

He traced the full curve of her upper lip with his tongue. She tasted sweet. He could feel the trembling starting in her and wanted to see her eyes, to know how they would look when he possessed her, loved her in the way a man loves a woman. He whispered raggedly, 'Did you think about the water...patterns of light on water...the mountains...the sky?'

He drew his lips along her cheekbone, felt a nerve fluttering under his kiss. Her eyelids drooped, then lifted as she struggled to remember how the ocean had looked, whether the hills had been green or rocky. Desire for her, need, surged over him with an immediacy he hadn't thought possible. He gasped, drawing her closer, knowing he was close to losing control, unwilling to draw back.

'Crystal?' He dragged her name out, the desires of his body fighting with the caution that should have been second nature, that had always been the first thing...until her.

Her eyes flew to his. He could see the uncertainty, a vague alarm in them. He said carefully, 'Crystal, you know that I want you?'

Her eyes shied away and he wondered how experienced she actually was. She had been married, seemed a modern woman, yet the shyness worried him. She twisted on the sleeping-bag and he could feel the curves pressing against his side. He wanted to push her back, to see her lying there beneath him, her hair spread in a cloud of fire, her eyes drugged with desire for him. He wanted to touch her, to kiss her everywhere, to send her mad with loving and needing. He gave himself up to the wonderful insanity she stirred in him, closed his hand on her hip and pulled her close against him.

She was wild honey, the taste and the feel of ecstasy. Her tongue was soft, then firm, touching his, exploring. A man could go mad loving a woman like this. His fingers found the buttons of his jacket where they closed around her, then her blouse. Her breasts were covered with a lacy delicacy teasing his fingertips. He touched softly, feeling the gentle roughness of the lace, her breathless gasp as his thumb found the rising rigidity of her nipple.

She was warmer, even softer than he remembered, her gasp more shattering to the wildness rising inside him. Impossible, but this would be even better than the erotic dream-memory haunting him. He found his lips on the softness above her lacy bra, searching, tongue touching.

His hands urged her closer, his body joyfully accepted the thrust of her hip and thigh as he gloried in her wild sweetness, impossibly trapped against him.

His fingers fumbled like a young boy's, seeking the freedom of her softness. Then her breasts sprang free, the lacy bra falling away as the front closure was released. He buried his face in her firm softness, gentled against her as she gasped. He was careful even in his aching desire, not wanting to burn her sensitive whiteness with the rough growth of his beard.

He dragged his eyes open, a deep wonder filling him as he found her head thrown back, her lips parted, her eyelids almost closed. She needed him, ached for him. For a moment his hands smoothed back her hair, his lips seeking hers, possessing deeply. Then he felt the thrust of her breasts against him, her silent message, and he bent again to pleasure her with his mouth.

His hands took their own path as his lips and tongue explored her upper body. Fingers found the smooth trembling at her midriff, the button that held at her waist. Trembling, fumbling, his desire growing beyond control, he felt the fabric part as he slid the zipper down, then he smoothed the fabric away, feeling her slender tension against him, drawing her closer, closer, until the barrier of his clothing and her lacy panties seemed unbearable.

'Crystal...' Her fingers were under his shirt, probing the ridges of his back. He touched her warmth and felt her fingers go slack and weak. He slid his hands under the fabric, felt the faint roundness of her belly, and it was like a shaft of pain through him, the need to give her a child, to feel his seed growing in her.

'Jesse,' she whispered, and he fought back the dizziness. He pulled her closer, knowing it was wrong, that he must protect her. Her hand slid all along the ridge of his spine and he groaned, knowing he must stop, and that he could not.

'Honey, I....' The softness of her breast teased his lips as they moved, and he took the swelling peak deep into his mouth, heard her groan as she tensed against him, her hands wild on him, her hips twisting, searching. 'Oh, God! Honey, I——'

'Don't,' she whispered, her thigh pushing between his. 'Please don't talk.'

Talk. Love. He could feel every shudder that possessed her body. His touch. His lips. Her heat. She was wonderful, all that warmth trapped when she pretended to be cool and rational, an accountant who didn't do silly things, didn't see the scenery.

'Have to talk,' he dragged out, not wanting to fight the dizziness, the purposeful strength that surged through him when he looked down at the smooth white of her rosy-tipped breasts, her abdomen softly rounded between the twin thrusts of her hips. God, those panties should be X-rated!

He took her lips, heard her groan softly, 'Jesse, I want you.'

He managed to say hoarsely, 'Wanting isn't exactly the only issue, honey.' His fingers brushed her hair back, found the tender flesh at the back of her jaw, caressed her ears and wanted more. 'I don't know when I've wanted a woman the way you make me want you.' He groaned. 'You're magic, honey, but I've got no way to protect you, and—I spend my life flying all over hell. My life-style doesn't exactly suit marriage or children.' As he said the words, he was overcome by a vision of Crystal lying in his big bed at home, a baby lying beside her, nursing at her breast. He said, 'Honey, I——' But he did not know what words he wanted to tell her. He felt her move against him and knew that he would take her if she reached out and caressed him with that warmth.

He couldn't tell what was beneath the sudden deep green in her hazel eyes as she whispered, 'I told you, I don't want a man in my life. Didn't I tell you that?'

His fingers traced the arch of her eyebrow, his eyes troubled as they probed hers. His pulse was steadying. He wanted her, heaven knew! But this was wrong, his hands telling her love. She was meant for a home, family. She should have loving all around her, permanence. He tried to tell her. 'You weren't made to be alone, honey. You should find a man, have another child.' He could see her face closing, something shutting him out, and he said raggedly, 'That's what worries me. The other night—that wasn't planned.' Was it possible that his child already grew inside her? He swallowed, not sure if he felt alarm or joy. 'I don't think you're prepared for——'

Her voice broke harshly over him. 'I can't have children. The accident——' and he knew a sudden sick disappointment, irrational and overwhelming. Tomorrow it would be a relief, but right now it hurt that his loving could not create life in her. It hurt her, too. She was drawing away from him, the warmth going. Her eyes were dark, hurting, and he closed her lids with his lips, tasting the salt of tears. Her mouth opened and he moved to take the words from her.

'Don't talk,' he whispered, echoing her words. 'Let me love you.'

He heard her clear her throat. 'Jesse, I didn't—what I told you, that's not——'

'Shh.' She was shivering. He wanted only to make her warm. The desire was dampened in him, overcome by the need to comfort her. He touched her very gently. When her lips parted without words, he drew her close.

Between them, slowly, the heat grew, a soundless pulsing that welled up, given and received, their limbs tangling, mouths caressing, fingers and hands touching, knowing, needing. Then the barriers were gone, the harshness of fabric discarded, tossed away heedlessly.

As the sun moved lower in the sky, shafting light through the trees on to their naked bodies, she moved to him and he covered her. Then he made her his, and it felt like eternity exploding around them, the end and the beginning.

CHAPTER SEVEN

CRYSTAL woke knowing that he was watching her. She opened her eyes and found his face close, turned towards her, his eyes lazy in the early morning.

'Hello,' she said softly, watching his eyes, liking the way the black shifted to a deep brown as he looked at her. 'Can I get you breakfast? Bacon and eggs?' He laughed then, and she grinned. 'You don't like bacon? Pancakes, maybe? Or a light breakfast? Grapefruit and toast?'

'You,' he said, growling low, touching, stirring what seemed to lie ready for him always, just below the surface of her skin.

She closed her eyes, letting the feeling of this man overwhelm her, hoping the child would look like him, the dark hair curling everywhere, the eyes black and fathomless. She wished she hadn't lied to him, wondered if she could somehow tell the truth now, but then he touched her with his lips and the need to love overcame everything else.

Afterwards they ate, huckleberries and water, their laughter ringing through the quiet wilderness.

Then the ravine.

'We have to cross it,' Jesse decided after exploring both uphill and downhill from their campsite. She waited, silent while he worried at the problem. 'The net,' he said finally, frowning at her.

'You're going to string it across? We're going to climb it?' She thought she could do anything he asked of her, but the idea of crossing that ravine on a flimsy fishing net made her faith founder.

'No. We'll climb down. I think you can get down if I help you.' She nodded, knowing she could do anything if he helped her. He continued, 'Then I'll climb up...' he stared across, frowning '...somehow, then I'll hang the net down for you to climb on.'

He made it sound like a ladder, and she followed him down the steep drop to the bottom, edging from one foothold to the next, blissfully ignorant of the horrifying ascent to come. Then he left her alone while he took the net and climbed up and away from her. She stood alone in the shadows, watching, the sides looming up around her, seeming to rise to the heavens.

Once, a shower of small rocks came tumbling down. He shouted, 'Look out! Stay out from under me!' and she jumped back, horrified that he would fall with the rocks. After that she crouched on a rock at the bottom of the cliff, staring up as he went higher and higher. He would fall. He would lose his grip and come plummeting to the bottom. Then he would be on the rocks, broken and dead.

Yet the waiting was endless. The watching left her panic stricken, the adrenalin coursing through her veins, urging her to action while she was trapped down here. Immobile. She wished she could look away, stop watching his legs high above her. She wished the horrifying fantasies would stop. Then, suddenly, his legs were gone and she was alone in the world.

'Jesse?' She hadn't meant to send up such a desperate scream, but the panic was overwhelming. She was closed in, trapped by dark, high walls. Claustrophobia. Panic.

'I'm here! Hold on!' His voice was strong and sure, although she could not see him. 'I'm just stringing the net. Take it easy, honey!' Where was he? Why couldn't she see him? 'Just take a deep breath and hold on a few minutes.'

Then his head appeared, his face strained as he looked down and asked, 'You OK?'

Yes. If he was there. Anything, so long as he did not leave her. She smiled shakily, said, 'What will you do if I'm not OK? What can you do from up there?'

He promised, 'I'll think of something,' and she believed him. She hugged herself, her arms gripping his jacket tightly against her, her voice worried. 'You must think I'm a phobic idiot. I'm not always like this, you know? I—really, Jesse, I don't run around like a Victorian female with the vapours, screaming at mice and terrified of everything.' She bit her lip, craned her neck to keep him in sight, then knew everything was all right when she heard his laughter.

'Climb up here and I'll tell you what I think of you.' His voice sounded odd. It must be some effect of the narrow gully on sound waves. 'Here, watch out! The net's coming down!'

The net spun down, unfolding lazily, falling towards her. When it stopped, it quivered over the rocks as it settled. 'Honey, how far above you is it? Can you reach it?'

'About my shoulders.' She touched it gingerly. It had held when she had pulled him from the ocean. Would it hold her now?

'It's secured up here around a big tree trunk. It's solid, and it's more than strong enough to hold you. Just take it easy, though. Use your hands and your feet and take it slowly.'

She wished there were water in this gully. She was desperately thirsty. Perhaps the mundane act of drinking would still the pounding in her chest. She swallowed and stared ahead, not up, and tried to think of a way out of this.

'What's the Spanish word for fishing net?' she asked him desperately.

'*Neto* something, I guess.' Above her, his voice was patient. 'Take your time. Don't start up until you're ready.'

'Don't you know what the Mexicans call their fishing nets?'

'Sorry. No.' He wasn't laughing. She wished he would laugh. 'I'll ask this winter and I'll let you know.'

'How did you get into flying?' she asked him, her voice desperate.

'Air cadets.' She heard something move overhead, his feet shifting on the ground. 'Take your time, honey. There's no rush.'

'Isn't there?' She tried laughing, but it didn't work. 'There's a rush in my head. Do they teach you to fly in air cadets?'

'I went to camp. They taught me to fly gliders. I was fifteen, and from then on I knew what I was going to do with my life.'

She clenched her hand on the net, pulled on it and felt it stretch down towards her. 'You didn't go to university?'

'No. Try one foot, honey. Just stick your foot into the mesh and slowly put your weight on. It will stretch a bit, then it'll stabilise once your weight is on it.'

She reached up high and clenched both hands around pieces of net. It was much thicker than the netting of Murray's hammock, although the weave seemed similar. When she pulled, it stretched, bringing the netting down lower. She took a deep breath, lifted her foot and slipped the moccasin through the netting.

Above her, Jesse's voice was casual. 'I borrowed the money from my brother to take flying lessons, then once I had my pilot's licence—are you all right?'

She had stopped, her body suspended like a spider on this crazy web. 'Yes. Just—it's kind of scary.' She bit her lip and moved her second foot off the ground. Everything shifted. She clenched on the moving net, found her foot groping wildly below her. She looked down, couldn't see her foot, but the ground was all rocks and sharp places under her. Only a couple of feet down, and she had for ever to go before the top.

'Just feel with your foot. Don't look down. Move your foot slowly, find a toehold.' She couldn't make sense of his words, but her limbs obeyed and slowly her spider web stabilised.

She shifted her handhold. First one hand, then the other. It didn't shift so alarmingly when she spread her arms and feet wider. God, she was terrified! She gulped, wanting to get out of this and knowing she could not. 'You got your pilot's licence, and then what? How old were you? Why your brother? What about your parents?' The questions spilled from her, a rush to push back fear.

'Our parents died when I was sixteen. A car accident.' So he knew the horror of loved ones suddenly taken on the highway. No wonder he had been so understanding. 'Harvey was already through university, had a good job. He did what he could to bring me up. I finished high school, went to university for a year, but Harvey couldn't afford that and it wasn't what I wanted.'

She managed another whole round of movement. One foot, then the other. Hands worked a little higher on the net. She clung to his voice and tried not to think about what was below her, or what above.

'You're doing well.' Did he sound closer? She tipped her head back and he said, 'No, just concentrate on what's in front of you. Take it easy and I'll tell you about my young life.'

'You're thirty-five if you're a day,' she snapped, getting the hands shifted again, starting the sickening business of moving her feet. The net kept shifting, swinging sometimes so that she rubbed painfully against the rocks it lay against. 'Some people might call you middle-aged.'

'But you wouldn't. Not after last night.' His voice was closer. She could swear it was. She bit her lip and concentrated on the net. Her fingers were hurting. The net seemed even to cut through the thick fabric of her makeshift moccasin.

'How can you laugh when I'm stuck here on the side of a cliff?' Her hands were cramping. She flexed the fingers and they held.

'It isn't easy.' His voice was husky, then stronger. 'I went up north after I got my pilot's licence.'

'To Prince Rupert?' She couldn't find the holes in the net, couldn't feel through the moccasin.

'No. Prince Rupert is north for you, but for me it was my home town. I went to the Yukon and got a job with a small charter company up there, working in the office, begging all the flying hours I could get until I had my commercial licence—— Easy, honey. There's not much farther. No, don't look up! Just keep going.'

'The story of my life,' she muttered. 'Just keep going.' Her hands weren't going to last much longer. Every time she let a piece of net loose, the fingers refused to start curling closed again. 'After you had your licence, what?'

'I flew for that company for a while, saved my money. Then I came back home and bought a couple of planes.' She could hear the shrug in his voice. 'Chased after business. Mining contracts. Supplying isolated logging companies. Flying people in and out of the villages. After a while, there were regular customers, then more business than I could handle.'

'It's been growing ever since?' The office had looked busy. She felt cautiously for the next foothold, tried to concentrate on estimating how much business went through that office of his in a week, a month. That kind of estimation should be second nature. She was always doing it, making mental guesses from the evidence, confirming it with the records, the books and the bank transactions.

'I don't really want to push it too much bigger. It's a good living, and I'm pretty free of bank loans and such. If I expand much more, I could be pretty vulnerable if the economy takes a downturn.'

'You sound like an accountant.' She almost laughed, but she was far too frightened.

'Probably I'm reflecting some of Lucy's advice. Easy, honey. Stop when you're tired. Just relax and take a few deep breaths. There's no hurry.'

She paused, staring at a point of rock about three inches in front of her eyes. Her hands were cramping. Her knee was starting to hurt. Relax? The man was insane.

'I'm afraid of heights,' she whispered. She had been on a chairlift once, and it had been living terror. 'Jesse, I'm not good at this. I can't make it.'

His voice was strong, confident. 'You're almost there. Don't think about up or down, just one hand at a time, one foot, and then the other. Now move your left foot. Up a little higher. There!'

She was moving again. She didn't think she could do it for much longer, but she did not want to disappoint him when he seemed so sure that she could make it.

'Did you never want to get married?' She was staring at a horribly sharp piece of rock. She could see the net straining over it, the green strands separating.

He said, 'I almost did get married, years ago.'

'What happened? What was she like?' Did he still think about her, the woman he had not married?

She could hear his shrug. 'She wanted me to quit flying, to stay behind the desk and quit at five every night.' He was silent, then, 'There's no reason she couldn't have that. She was a nice girl and she wanted a man who came home on time. It was just that I couldn't do it for her.'

She knew about that, about people who asked impossible things. David, wanting her to remain frozen as the seventeen-year-old girl he had married. Her eyes locked on the section of net in front of her and she called up desperately, 'Jesse, this rock is cutting the net!'

'Easy, it's all right.' She quieted her breathing, still staring at the rock. 'Honey, the net is wide, about six feet if we stretch it out that way. If one strand wears through, the sections around it will hold.'

'You sound so damned logical,' she gritted. She was the one who was usually so logical, a good auditor. She shifted her leg. The knee was aching where she had fallen on it. She froze as the motion sawed the net across the rock edge, then she screamed.

'Jesse!'

'Easy, honey, just tell me what's happening.'

'The net.' He sounded so damned calm. 'I'm sorry, I—— The rock cut through, but you were right. It's OK.'

'Tell me how you got into tax auditing.'

'Now?' In the middle of the cliff, in what were probably her last minutes?

'Why not?' He sounded as if he had all the time in the world up there. 'You've nothing else to do right now, have you?'

'Just climbing this spider web.' Another hand. Her fingers went through the net, closed on rock that crumbled to nothing. She caught at the net with a desperate hand. 'I took a course,' she gasped.

'In tax auditing?'

'No.' There. She had gone two more steps up. It was getting easier now. 'Johnny was in kindergarten and I wanted to do something. I felt that I had been home for ever. I married David the week after I graduated, and then my life turned into just—I loved having Johnny, it wasn't that, but I really was starting to feel I wanted more.'

The net—no, not there. Her fingers couldn't get a grip with the rock pushing through. She shifted and found an easier place to grab, wondered if this would ever end, wondered how far there was left to go.

Above her, Jesse's voice made her guilty rebellion against David seem almost reasonable. 'You don't have to be defensive about that, honey. Why shouldn't you want to develop your own talents?'

The kitchen. That was where they had had the worst row, her screaming and David walking out, not returning until morning. Johnny stumbling out of bed, standing in the hallway in his pyjamas, crying because he had woken too quickly and did not understand the anger in their voices.

'David didn't want me to go to work, but I—he finally agreed to let me go back to classes. We had a terrible fight. He said—I said I would leave him, and he walked out, and I thought I would never see him again.' She had been terrified, knowing she could not support herself and Johnny, yet at the same time feeling an excitement that maybe, just maybe she could reach out and be somebody on her own now. She realised that Jesse was silent, waiting and she said finally, 'He came back the next day. He never mentioned it again except to ask me how much I needed for fees and books. I took the bookkeeping course. He hated it, but he paid for me. He used to turn the television up when I was studying, but he didn't say anything again.' She had never told anyone about that before, not even Murray.

She reached her hand up and found the next handhold hanging out a little. She wondered if she would still be with David if the accident had not happened. She was afraid to look up, afraid she would see that the rest of the climb was impossible.

'And then you got a job?' Jesse's voice, prodding her on.

'I—no. David hated the idea of my working, and I wasn't up to another fight. I registered as a business administration student.'

She concentrated on finding a place for her foot to move. When she stopped to rest for a minute she realised that he was silent. 'Jesse? Are you still there?'

'I'm here.' His voice sounded warm, blessedly close. 'I'm just having a little trouble with the concept of you as a downtrodden housewife. I expect you've changed a bit in the last few years.'

'I guess I have.' David wouldn't like the way she was now. 'I went to work after the accident. Not at first, but—when Murray bullied me into looking for work. I had my business certificate, and Revenue Canada was advertising about then for people for the audit department. I applied for jobs, and that was the one I got.' She would have shrugged if it hadn't been for the way her hands and arms ached from holding her. 'So I registered with CGA to finish the courses I needed by correspondence, and I became an auditor.'

Ahead of her the rock face thrust out. She had been afraid of this, that she would have to go out, hanging over nothing on the net. 'Jesse?'

'Take your time. Stop for a minute. Take a deep breath and——'

'I can't! I can't do it, Jesse.' She closed her eyes tightly. 'Talk to me, please. I—Jesse, I'll close my eyes and hang on. Can't you just pull me up? I can't do this! I really——'

'I can't pull you up, honey. The rocks are too sharp. The net would catch, and—— Take a minute to get ready, then get moving again. You can do your trembling after you're up.'

'You're a bastard,' she whispered.

She knew it was not true, but she was so horribly frightened of taking the next step. If she didn't do it soon, her fingers would open and she would fall. She closed her eyes, then opened them because she had to see. One hand, then the other. Her legs swung out then, still attached to the net but swinging free in the air. She couldn't move her feet. Her hands would not hold.

Above her, fingers locked around her wrists, holding her bruisingly tight. He shouted, 'Turn your hands and hold on to my wrists!' She did, giving up her hold on the net, feeling his pulse under her palm, her tightened fingers on his wrist reinforcing his secure grip of her.

'Now your feet.' His voice was strong and hard. 'Climb, Crystal! Help me.'

She scrambled with her legs as he pulled her up, and then she was safe in his arms, shaking and crying. 'I'm not cut out for this,' she told him weakly. 'I'm sorry, but I don't think I can do that again.'

'You won't have to. I promise you that you won't have to.' His laugh was only a breath, nerves rather than amusement. 'I don't think I could handle watching. I think I was more frightened than you were.'

He released her slowly as she moved away. She laughed too then, shakily, looking down and not believing she had come all that way. 'Next time,' she advised him wryly, 'next time you decide to crash a plane, I think you should pick a more suitable passenger for the adventure.'

He was looking out towards the water. From here you could actually see the ocean, or the arm of it that separated Princess Royal Island from whatever that hill was across the way. She felt her nerves calming and she asked, 'What's that hill? Another island?'

'The mainland.' He was looking away, frowning at the mountain she had asked him to identify. 'As for a suitable passenger, I don't think I could pick anyone better.' He stiffened, his eyes intent on the patterns of water and mountains. 'See that island in the middle of the channel? That's Work Island. It's right opposite Butedale.'

She felt a sickening lurch in her stomach. Not yet! She wasn't ready to be rescued yet. 'How far?'

'A couple of miles.' He looked down at her, his eyes sombre. 'I think we'd better go on, honey. Now.'

She wanted to tell him her knee hurt, that she could not walk. He stopped, not moving despite his words, staring at her, catching deep inside her with his eyes. When his voice came again, it was low and shaken.

'I think it's time we got out of here, honey. Both of us. Before we get into more than we bargained for.'

He picked up the sleeping-bag, arranged it again over his shoulders with the net as a harness. Then he turned and started walking, not looking back, as if he knew she would follow. Or as if he did not care. She stumbled after him, wishing the going were not suddenly so easy, as if the path were made for them.

He was saying, 'If we're lucky, we'll find our way to the stairs that go up from the town to the lake. That would make the last part easier.' He talked as if their route were clear in his mind. 'If everything goes as it should, we'll be out of here today.'

Of course it was what she wanted, too. The night before belonged with the rest of this adventure, with the impossible dreams that were unfolding inside her. She would follow him, stumbling in his wake as if she were willing to follow to the end of the world. Then it would be over, and she would be back into the other life.

She wasn't going to miss him. At least . . . surely she would not feel it with the ache she had felt as he turned away a moment ago? Once she was back to normal, had her own life around her again, it would be all right.

The sun climbed higher. He walked without talking. She wished he would talk to her, the conversation she had grown used to as they moved slowly along the edges of this massive island . . . No. Silence was better. She had to get ready for the world, find her way back to the Crystal she had been when she stepped on to that Cessna.

When he stopped, she slowed, coming up beside him. Another gully? Or a bear? She found that the idea of a bear was not all that disturbing, but a gully to climb——

'Here they are! The stairs!' The stairs. They were old and unsteady. Just stairs stretching from up there . . . down. Down for ever, disappearing in the trees. Beside the stairs, a massive wooden pipe leaked water in small geysers. Butedale was somewhere down the stairs.

'What's the pipe?' she asked, not caring, feeling a dullness growing inside her.

'The penstock. It carries the water from the lake down to the generators below. Butedale has its own hydro-electric plant. A ghost town with lights.' He moved, the stairs creaking under his feet. There was a rail, although in places it was fragile.

'I feel like a squaw,' she mumbled to his back. 'Following two steps behind.'

She thought that yesterday he would have laughed, turned and said something to her with his eyes. He seemed different now. Sombre. He just shrugged and kept descending steps, leading the way.

Was he eager to be rid of her? She had made a fool of herself climbing that cliff. She had been terrified. She glowered at his back and told herself she hoped that he ended up with a muscle-bound woman who knew how to climb mountains and looked ugly as sin.

Maybe Murray was right. She should open up a bit. When she got home, she would work on it. She would date a little more often. She wasn't going to get married again, but there could be a man sometimes. Just for dinner and an evening. Talking. Otherwise her apartment would be very lonely, and her dreams would fill with Jesse.

She thought of her apartment, of the houses all around. She was going to miss this, the trees and the sounds, the green everywhere. She was going to miss Jesse, too.

The stairs went for ever, down and down. She could hear a roaring that grew with each step. Then, suddenly, there was a building. 'The generators!' Jesse shouted over the noise. 'There's a little bridge here! Be careful!'

He seemed to expect everything to be rotten, the wood giving way. There was a town, empty shells of buildings

on the hillside. Across the rooftops she could see one
building that seemed to be sliding down the hill, as if a
child had knocked a toy house on its side and left it
there.

He took her hand. She felt her fingers curling around
his as if they belonged there. Then they walked slowly
down a wide footpath, on to a massive pier that strutted
out raggedly over a bay. Much of the pier was gone,
boards rotted away and fallen through towards the ocean.
Parts of it were roped and fenced off.

Jesse led her along the edge, close against the
buildings, moving towards a red metal ramp that led
down at a frightening angle towards the water.

'I don't see any evidence of caretakers, but there's a
fishing boat tied up down there.'

Her fleeting hope drained away, that they would find
the place deserted. She followed down the ramp, wondering what life would feel like when she was walking
alone again, not looking down at the ground and the
back of Jesse's jeans, looking up at his black head, his
strong shoulders just a couple of steps ahead of her.

At the bottom of the ramp he took four long strides
across and a fisherman looked up from where he was
untying his lines from the dock.

Jesse smiled and said, 'Can I use your radio?'

The old fisherman's eyes took in Jesse, the wild hair,
the beard, then the torn jeans, the makeshift footwear.
The sharp eyes slid on to Crystal and there was no sur-
prise in them. As if this happened every day, wild people
walking out of the bush and up to his boat.

He jerked his head and said, 'In there. In the cockpit.'
Jesse disappeared into the boat. The fisherman ex-
amined Crystal with leisurely eyes. 'You're from that
plane that went missing?'

'Yes.' She sagged against the ramp. She didn't have to walk any more. She dropped down cross-legged on the float, not caring what this man thought.

'Walked out, did you?' His brows were thick, with long white hairs twisting down over his eyes.

'Yes.' It seemed to be all she could say. Yes. She wondered if there would be a place where she could have a bath or a shower soon. And what about clothes? Everything she had brought was underwater, gone with the Cessna and her audit-bag.

Her audit-bag! How could she have walked for days with hardly a thought of it? She looked down and saw what the fisherman was seeing. Jesse's cut-up jacket buttoned over her own tattered blouse. Her slacks, suitable for nothing but the dustbin now. The dirty fabric tied around her feet.

'Would you like a cup of coffee?' Incredibly, the man was holding out a steaming mug.

'Oh, yes!' She accepted it, holding it in her hands and feeling the warmth, drawing in the aroma. 'Thank you!'

'Cigarette?' he asked, offering a pack.

She extended her hand towards him. 'Thanks. I—no, I guess I won't.' She grinned, remembering how she had wanted a smoke the morning after the crash. 'I guess I quit.' It would be simpler at work with the non-smoking regulations that were taking over everything.

He grinned, reminding her a little of Jesse. 'Rotten habit,' he agreed. 'I should give it up. I'm Slim.'

He was long and very lean, so she supposed the nickname was deserved. She smiled unsteadily, said, 'Hi, Slim. I'm Crystal. What day is it?'

'Saturday. October—ah—the third.'

The Queen Charlotte audits would be over by now. It had been planned as a quick, routine review, and someone else would have been sent in to take her place.

When Jesse returned he seemed brisker, quicker, as if the conversation on the radio had rested and refreshed him. 'Thanks,' he said to Slim. 'I got through.'

The fisherman nodded. 'Need anything else? A ride somewhere? I was just leaving. Just stopped for a few hours' sleep.'

'That's OK. The helicopter will be along in a few minutes. Thanks.' A few minutes. That was all they had. Just minutes, seconds. Since the crash time had seemed like for ever, now suddenly things were happening, moving too quickly. She watched as Jesse helped Slim untie his lines. Jesse seemed indifferent to the passage of two or three more of their precious minutes.

'Your cup!' Crystal called after the fisherman as he powered his boat away from the float. 'I've still got your cup!'

'Forget it!' He was grinning, waving at them both. 'Give the pilot a sip, and keep the cup!'

As the sound of the fishing boat's engine died away, she held out the cup to Jesse. He accepted it and lifted it to his lips. She watched as he sipped, closing his eyes as the liquid slid down his throat.

'Good?' she asked, enjoying his pleasure.

'Wonderful! Never thought I'd enjoy black coffee that much.'

She could hear a noise growing, a rhythm that beat against the sky. Surely not the helicopter already? 'You said a couple of minutes? The helicopter? What helicopter?'

She thought he was going to reach out and touch her, but his hand went instead to rake through his hair. 'I got hold of the coastguard station. The rescue chopper was searching just north of us, so he's on his way now.'

The big orange and white machine descended out of the sky, tipping sideways and dropping down on to the water, landing on pontoons and moving somehow up against the end of the wharf. Then a door opened and Jesse was holding her, helping her into the machine, other men touching her, pressing her down, belting her into a seat-belt while the door closed and they lifted, rising quickly, slanting away from the trees and the water.

She thought Jesse would sit beside her, but he was up ahead. She could see him talking to the crew, but could not hear the words. Once he laughed, then he frowned and explained something, his hands gesturing. When he turned and pointed down through the window, the helicopter pilot took the helicopter down.

She knew he was showing them where the plane had sunk. Evidently, there was no sign in the water, because they rose up again, sweeping on to the north. She willed him to look at her, but he was totally involved in talking to the helicopter crew. One of the men was asking him questions and he was answering, and everyone was smiling because the crash victims were here and alive and the search was over.

It seemed no time before she saw the town, the harbour laid out below her. They flew over the buildings, sweeping up to a hill in the middle of the town, then descending.

Then the insanity started. The doors opened and white-coated people appeared. A tall, blonde woman in white threw herself into Jesse's arms, chiding him. 'Jesse, I thought you'd killed yourself!'

Someone was pressing her into a stretcher, but she could hear Jesse laughing gently at the blonde, saying, 'Behave yourself, girl! You're supposed to be ministering to me, checking me out for broken bones and hypothermia.'

She didn't see him again. White-coated men were carrying her stretcher, ignoring her protests, rushing away from the helicopter and into what seemed to be the emergency department of a hospital. She didn't realise that she was crying until a woman stood over her and said gently, 'It's all right. You're going to get some food and some rest, then you'll feel a lot better.'

'I don't need——' Food. The thought made her feel nauseous and hungry, both at once. 'I'm OK, Nurse. I don't need to be here.'

'I'm a doctor,' the woman said, then ran cool hands over Crystal, finding painful places that hadn't existed until the doctor touched. It was no use. The medical establishment had hold of her, and there was no way to fight. They would do their will. She tried again briefly as someone wheeled her into a private room.

'I don't need a private room.' Her budget was going to be strained as it was, replacing her audit-bag, the computer and her clothes. The insurance charge for a private room was more than she needed. 'I'm——'

'Don't worry about it.' This nurse seemed impossibly young. 'Relax and let us look after you. You're a celebrity, you know.'

'Why? The crash?'

The tattered blouse joined Jesse's jacket on the floor. The nurse said, 'The crash is nothing compared to what you two did. People just don't walk out through those bushes. Not in this part of the world. When it happens, the heroes deserve a bit of coddling.' She pulled out a thin nightgown from a cupboard, said, 'I know you want a shower, but you're going to have to wait for that.'

The room. The hands tending to her, washing and putting her to bed. Then the indignity of an intravenous needle when what she really should have was solid food. She accepted the sleeping pill, although she never took pills. Then, when they pulled the curtains and turned out the lights, she obeyed the voice that told her to go to sleep. It was easier than fighting, and there seemed little to stay awake for when Jesse did not seem to have any intention of visiting her, when a long-legged, beautiful blonde had cried when she saw him alive.

She woke suddenly as the door to her room swung open. She remembered opening her eyes in the night, accepting a pill of some unknown kind from someone in white. Then morning, a thermometer and another pill, long swallows of cool water through a straw. Now half the day seemed to be gone and she was awake, staring at the brightly dressed woman coming through the door.

'Hi!' The woman seemed to bring energy with her into the hospital room. Her short auburn curls bounced as she stopped at the foot of Crystal's bed. 'I'm Lucy McGraw. Jesse sent me to see how you were doing.'

'You're Jesse's accountant?' Crystal shifted higher in the bed, discovered that someone had taken the intravenous needle out of her arm. She was glad. It reminded her too much of that other hospital stay, after the accident.

'That's right,' Lucy agreed, grinning. 'I hadn't thought of it, but maybe that's why Jesse sent me. You're a tax auditor?'

Crystal couldn't resist this woman's smile. 'You mean we'd get on together? Talk debits and credits?'

The red curls bounced. 'Something like that. I brought you clothes. Jesse said we were about the same size, but I brought things that wouldn't matter too much if he was wrong.' Crystal watched as Lucy opened a door, found a hanger and carefully arranged a denim wraparound skirt and a bright cotton blouse on it. 'If you're a bit taller than me, or shorter, it shouldn't matter too much in this. I brought shoes—sandals, because if your feet are different than mine, the straps should give a bit.

And underwear.' She slipped a new packet of tights out of her bag, put them on the bedside-table, then grinned and added a small bag. 'Jesse didn't tell me your bra size, but you can try that. If it doesn't work out, you can always go braless. I often do when I wear that blouse.'

'Thank you.' Crystal could feel the flush on her face, a response to the assumption that Jesse would be likely to know intimate things like her bra size. 'I—thanks. I didn't know how I was going to get out of here. The clothes I was wearing were pretty much a write-off.'

'I can imagine.' Lucy pulled up a chair and settled lightly on to it, as if she might move again at any second. Crystal decided that this woman was incurably restless. She probably had twice as many clients as most accountants, and served them all well. Was this the kind of woman that appealed to Jesse? A woman filled with energy, a passionate person. But Jesse had said she was married, hadn't he? And he had the blonde, or did he?

'Is there anything else I can get for you? I brought a toothbrush, and toothpaste. They're in the bag.' Lucy grinned. 'And the latest CGA magazine. It came to me in the mail today. There's an article in it on the new tax reform, so I thought you might be interested in it. I brought a couple of other books, too. A romance. And a mystery.'

'Thank you. I—there's nothing else. I—— How is Jesse? Did they bring him into the hospital?'

'Yes. Overnight. I guess it's standard practice. Jesse tried to talk them out of it and was told to shut up and behave himself. Yes, I thought you'd find that amusing,' she said as Crystal laughed. 'Is there anything else I can do for you?'

She shook her head and Lucy said, 'You were on the radio this morning—pilot and beautiful passenger walk out through dense coastal bush after near-death experience!'

'Oh, no!' If her mother heard that, she would be frantic. 'My mother——'

'Jesse looked after that. Apparently a fellow named Murray has been burning up the phone lines to the seaplane base. Jesse said to tell you he talked to him this morning, assured him you were fine. Then he got your mom's phone number and your boss's. He called them both, told your mother you were fine, told your boss you'd be back at work in no time.'

She relaxed, glad that she didn't have to do anything yet. 'That was good of him. Thank him for me, please.'

'He's a thoughtful man, but you'll have lots of time to thank him yourself. Look, here's my phone number at work. Get them to call me if there's anything you need.' She grinned, added, 'That is, anything that isn't in Jesse's province.'

It was in Lucy's eyes, the knowledge that she and Jesse had been lovers. What had Jesse said? That he would probably tell her, or she would guess. Had he told her? She said unwillingly, 'Lucy, when we flew in here there was a nurse——'

Lucy nodded, said, 'Charlie. She told me she was on emergency when you and Jesse flew in.'

'I—we really aren't——' Charlie. She had a name, and Lucy knew about her, talked to her. 'I've got to get back home, back to work.'

Lucy picked up her bag. 'Surely not today? It's Sunday. I'm working, because Max and I are overrun with new jobs at the moment, and Jesse is, because he can't stay away from the seaplane base and he's got reams to do after losing that plane. But surely government employees don't have to work Sundays, especially just after they walk out of the bush.'

Crystal looked down at her own idle hands. They were bruised and filled with tiny scratches. 'What am I supposed to do? Sit here in the hospital?'

'Jesse talked to the doctor. She says you can go home this afternoon if you're feeling OK when she does her afternoon rounds. I'll come back and pick you up and drive you to Jesse's.'

'Why are you doing all this? Is this what an accountant normally does for a client?'

'Jesse's more than a client. Neighbour...friend...my daughter's favourite babysitter.' She shrugged. 'I'd do almost anything to keep a good babysitter. You will call if you need something? And I'll pick you up about four this afternoon.'

Then she was gone, leaving Crystal to reconcile the image of the Jesse she knew with Lucy McGraw's babysitter.

CHAPTER EIGHT

'IT'S in here somewhere.' Lucy twisted herself into a corner of the garage and emerged triumphant with the doorkey. 'Of course, if I were Jesse, I'd just reach in a long arm—the advantages of being tall! The rest of us have to crawl into the corner.'

'The rest of us?' Crystal had a feeling that the world was going to be too much for her. Her mind had grown accustomed to a basic reality—the bushes...the bears...Jesse.

Lucy slung her bag back over her arm and led the way to a massive front door—or back door. Crystal was not sure which. The house was large, too large for one man, but it seemed to have its back facing the street. Come to that, it wasn't on the street at all, but up a steep driveway that wound through the trees. Unlike the other houses on Seal Cove Circle, Jesse Campbell's home was invisible, unless you came up here looking for him.

'The rest of us,' the accountant repeated, shaking the curls back and laughing with her eyes. She turned the key without looking, as if she did it every day. 'There's Max and I, next door. Over there.' She gestured towards a wall of trees. 'Then Charlie, of course...and Keith and David and Bonnie.' She shrugged, the door opening before her. 'Whoever else is around with—— Oh, and the girls! Here they are!'

Crystal knew about the girls. The cats, not his daughters. They were twisting around Lucy's ankles, a beautiful Siamese and a very ordinary tabby.

'Siam and Tabby,' said Lucy. 'Jesse has no imagination when it comes to naming the beasts. Don't believe them when they say they're starving. I fed them all the time you guys were out gallivanting in the bushes, and Jesse fed them this morning. They always put on that starving act.'

Crystal couldn't think of anything to say. It didn't seem to matter. Lucy just kept talking. 'The house is upstairs. Down here is just Charlie's, and of course the landing. You'll meet her later, I'm sure. Make yourself at home. That's Jesse's instructions. He says he'll be back as early as he can, but after being away it's hard for him to get loose of the seaplanes—people will have been saving up problems for him.'

'It's all right.' She pushed her hair back nervously. It felt clean again, but she still yearned for a shampooing and conditioning. Charlie lived here, with Jesse, and who was Bonnie? 'I—really, I should just go back to Vancouver right away.'

Lucy shook her head vigorously. 'Don't you dare! Jesse would have my head! He can be something fierce when he gets mad, so let's just do this the way he wants.' Lucy grinned. 'Why not? It's a lovely house. Enjoy a rest.' She looked around, her forehead creased slightly in a frown. 'Look, I hope you don't mind if I have to leave you? I have a computer having hysterics at the office, and Max needs help taming it.'

'Go ahead. Of course——'

'Help yourself to anything. Food. The bathtub. I bet that's what you'd like best. And tell Jesse we'll be over tonight. Don't worry about dinner. We'll bring something.' Crystal wanted to ask about Charlie, but Lucy was gone, a vivacious tornado, taking some of the light with her as she went.

Alone, she climbed wide, carpeted stairs that opened up into a broad expanse of brightness. It could have been a largish clearing in the outdoors, with the sky above and all around. That was the feeling she had, coming to the top of the steps and walking towards the window.

If you had to live indoors, this house came closest to pretending that the walls weren't there. Windows everywhere. A large balcony looking out over the hillside. Living-room and dining-room one big window on to the trees...the water...the hills on the far side of the harbour. Somehow the architect had arranged that not another house was in sight.

Leather chairs were positioned to look out while the sun set. That was west, wasn't it? Yes, it must be. This was the chair he used, its leather a little worn. Who sat in the other one? Charlie?

He had an Indian carving on the wall. A long, low chesterfield. Lots of room for guests here, although she could see him sitting comfortably alone, enjoying the ocean and the mountains. She thought of her own apartment, her concrete view. Going back was going to be like going into a cave, yet how could she live anywhere but the city? Her job was there, Revenue Canada's auditors firmly based in the densest part of Vancouver.

Should she think about leaving? With her CGA designation and her auditing experience, she could probably find a job in public practice. She shivered a little, knowing she would be afraid to walk away from the security of the last four years. And what if there was a child, Jesse's child? She couldn't take any chances with her salary then.

She wished that she could talk to Jesse about it when he came, but she had told the lie about being barren, and that made it impossible. She moved away from the windows, uncomfortable with the lie she had told, wondering what Jesse wanted of her, why she was here, why she had come.

The kitchen was like the rest of the house. Spacious, with modern conveniences that didn't intrude. Kettle handy on the stove... dishwasher... microwave oven. Did he do the cooking? She stepped carefully around the two cats twisting around her ankles, turned the kettle on and kicked her shoes—Lucy's shoes—off as she left the kitchen and went exploring.

Perhaps she would have a bath first, before the tea. She supposed she should find his telephone and call her mother and Murray, but she wanted to put her world off. Just one more day... a chance to say goodbye to Jesse, a leisurely goodbye to a man who had been... so much, yet for such a brief, endless period of time.

A man who said he wasn't married, but had a blonde named Charlie living under his roof. She bent and found herself stroking the soft tabby cat while the Siamese watched suspiciously.

The cats left the instant she turned on the water in the bathtub. Alone, she opened a cabinet at the foot of the tub and found an array of pampering supplies. Her hand hovered. Help yourself to anything, Lucy had said, but these things weren't Jesse's. They belonged to a woman. Charlie.

Crystal frowned and told herself that it didn't matter, that she was leaving and tomorrow Jesse Campbell would be nothing to her, only the memory of a few days that were unrelated to the rest of her life; and... maybe... the man who would never know he had given her a child. She used Charlie's shampoo and conditioner and wondered if she had just had a dizzying affair with a borrowed man. The thought left an unpleasant, metallic taste in her mouth.

She was sitting in his chair when she heard the door open. She had one hand tangled in the tabby's fur and the other holding a cup of tea. For a second she froze, as if this happened every night, her listening to the sound, knowing he would be here in a second. Then she remembered Charlie.

'Crystal?' His voice was clear. She thought his hand was still on the door. She didn't answer, just listened, heard the door close, then his footsteps running up the carpeted stairs.

'You are here!' He stopped, his hand on the banister, and she had the feeling that he was breathless as they stood, staring at each other. 'Why didn't you answer me?'

She shook her head, not knowing the answer, and he said, 'I thought you'd gone, honey,' his voice husky.

'Why did you bring me here?' She tried to stop the trembling of her teacup, watched his eyes and was afraid to wonder what she was looking for.

'I'm not sure.' His hand dropped from the banister. 'You look nice.' So did he. The jeans were gone, replaced by tailored dark trousers and a blue shirt that just showed under a light blue sweater. He was smiling, the curve of his lips making creases against his cheeks. 'I guess I just wasn't ready to say goodbye to you yet. How are you?'

'Fine.' She looked down at herself, the swirling skirt, the crisp blouse. 'Of course I'm fine. I'm clean. I had real food for lunch and there aren't any bears out in your bushes here, and—— Yes, I'm fine.'

She fell silent as he crossed the room towards her. 'I half thought you'd walk out of that hospital, fly away.' He frowned down at her, abruptly still in front of her. 'Why did you let Lucy bring you here?'

'I don't know.'

The low chuckle she remembered filled the room between them. 'I guess that makes us even. I don't why I had you brought here, and you don't know why you came, but there's one thing I am sure of.' His smile disappeared and her heart stopped as he said, 'I have this overwhelming urge to take you in my arms and find out if you're the same woman I remember.'

She saw his eyes turning molten, gulped and managed to say, 'I used your bathtub. I used somebody's bubble bath.'

'Charlie's.' He shrugged that away. 'Look, I'm going to take a quick shower myself. You won't go anywhere? I'll be ten minutes, then I'll get us something for supper—or would you like to go out to dinner?'

She shook her head, remembered, 'Lucy said she'd bring something, that they'd come over later.' When would Charlie come? Why didn't she have the guts to ask about Charlie? 'I should call the airlines and book a flight out of here. I have to——'

He touched her lips, silencing the flow of desperate words. 'Look, while I'm having a shower, why don't you make a list of what you lost in the crash? There's paper by the telephone, and a pen.'

Make a list? What did he expect, that she would put in a claim against him, sue him? Was this why he had brought her? To sweet talk her and prevent—oh, God! What if that had been it from the beginning? Making love to her, insurance against her causing him legal troubles later? She listened to the sounds of his shower, wondering what was in his mind. Was it the same as what she saw in his eyes? Or something else?

'Hey! You OK?'

She jerked, her eyes flying to the stairwell where a painfully thin teenage boy stood. His head was covered with Jesse's thick, unruly hair. He was motionless for a split second, shifting feet that were three sizes larger than the rest of him. Then he pushed his arms against the rail and seemed to shoot into the middle of the living-room.

'You're the lady Uncle Jesse dragged out of the bush?' He looked like a younger, shorter Jesse, and he must be Jesse's nephew. He said, 'Sorry. I didn't mean anything by that.'

She guessed he often spoke before he thought, and that not many people took offence. She grinned and said easily, 'It's OK. You're right. I'm Crystal Selwyn, the—the lady your uncle dragged out of the bush. Who are you?'

'Keith.' He was looking everywhere, into the kitchen, down the hallway. 'Hey, he's here, isn't he? I went to the base, but he was gone. My mom's likely to phone any minute, and I've got to talk to Uncle Jesse first.'

'He's in the shower.'

The boy's eyes swerved to the telephone and he shifted again nervously. 'If she phones, and I gotta answer——'

'You could take it off the hook,' suggested Crystal, trying not to smile.

He shook his head vigorously. 'He'd have my head if I did that. There might be an emergency, you see? Medical evacuation from some island, or a plane gone missing.' He veered away, going down the hallway towards the bathroom, shouting, 'Uncle Jesse? I gotta talk to you!'

She couldn't hear the response, but Keith came back along the passageway and slumped into the sofa, muttering, 'Hope he hurries.'

He shot to his feet as Jesse came out. He had changed into a lighter pair of trousers and a soft, loose sweater. His black hair was curling damply over his forehead, half-dry and brushed into submission. His eyes moved to Crystal's in a warm touch, then he stopped, looking down at Keith, a half smile on his lips.

'Trouble again?' he asked.

'Yeah.' Keith managed somehow to look angry and nervous at the same time. 'Look, can I stay the night?'

'Sure, if it's OK with your parents.' Crystal had the idea that he often stayed the night, that Jesse often asked, 'Do they know where you are?'

'No!' Keith paced across the room, unable to stay still for long. 'He—Uncle Jesse, I can't take it there! They're crazy, expecting me to behave like a little kid. I've got to get out, at least stay for dinner.'

Jesse didn't smile, although she had the feeling that he wanted to. His eyes met hers and there was some mixture of amusement and sympathy as he said to the boy, 'Well, then, call your parents and tell them where you are. Stay for dinner—the night, too, if you like.'

The boy hesitated. 'You—You couldn't call her, could you? I don't want to talk to him, and she'll be——'

'No,' said Jesse, and there was no doubt that he meant it. 'You're the one who has to talk to them.'

Keith stared at his uncle for a long minute, then shrugged and headed towards the stairs, throwing back, 'I'll use Charlie's phone.'

Jesse watched him go, then said quietly, 'He doesn't want us to hear him getting bawled out. He'll call. Harvey won't answer the phone, because he'll be too angry. My sister-in-law will order him home, and now that he's cooled off a bit he'll go.'

'Is it anything serious?'

Jesse shook his head. 'Minor explosions. You will have gathered that he's my nephew? Harvey, my brother, is pretty strict with him, so Keith's adolescence is stormy and filled with crises.'

Keith returned and proved Jesse right by announcing, 'I guess I'll go home. I've gotta clean out my room.' He shrugged, grimacing. 'See ya.'

Jesse offered, 'I'm flying out to the Queen Charlottes next weekend. Why don't you come with me, give me a hand with some of the cargo?'

'Yeah, I'd love to.' The boy's face lit with enthusiasm. 'Next weekend?'

'That's right. Come down to the base right after school Friday.'

'Super!'

The doorbell rang as Keith thundered down the stairs. Jesse ignored it, crossed to Crystal and extended his hand in an invitation. She found herself holding out her hand. His fingers clasped her warmly and drew her to her feet. The cat tumbled to the floor as she stood, then walked off in a huff when neither Jesse nor Crystal noticed.

He was close, his warmth invading her space, his dark eyes looking down on her with something between a frown and a smile. 'The doorbell,' she whispered.

He shook his head. 'I wanted to be alone with you.' He drew her closer with his hands around her upper arms. 'I—it seems to me that there's a lot that still needs to be—that we have unfinished business——'

He didn't sound like Jesse at all. He seemed uncertain, nervous. Then his lips covered hers and she forgot to question the strangeness in his eyes. Briefly, the world spun, and as his lips withdrew she could hear voices below.

'He's here.' That was Keith's voice, followed by a man's voice, lower, then Keith again, 'Naw. It's OK. They're not doing anything special.'

'I think it's special,' whispered Jesse, his hand slipping down her arm and taking possession of her curling fingers. 'Do you mind? They'll stay a while, then—later, we'll be alone.' She said nothing, staring up at him, wordless. What about Charlie? He turned and drew her with him as he went to meet his guests.

'Uncle Jethe!' The small, lisping ball of fire that flew up the stairs into his arms was no more than two years old. She seemed to know she had a welcome waiting, that he would drop Crystal's hand and hold out his arms to her and swing her high.

'Hi, my Bonnie,' he said, hugging her close, laughing with her as she sang tunelessly, 'My Bonnie lieth over the othon.'

Behind the little girl, Lucy was coming up the steps, holding hands with a lean, dark-haired man. Lucy seemed quieter now, as if the dark man stilled her to contentment.

'Looks as if you found your way around,' she greeted Crystal with a smile. 'This is Max, my husband. That's Bonnie, our daughter, squeezing the life out of Jesse.'

Jesse, still laughing, had lifted the girl on to his shoulders. She was gripping his hair tightly.

'Uncle?' said Crystal curiously.

'It's a courtesy title,' Lucy told her.

'Curthey?' asked Bonnie brightly, bending down from Jesse's shoulders.

Jesse's eyes met Crystal's. She said, 'I thought you lived alone except for a couple of cats. And Charlie.'

'Sort of,' he agreed. 'But——' He shrugged, jiggling Bonnie and looking slightly discomfited.

Lucy said, 'Jesse is everybody's uncle. He's a natural family man.' She grinned at him and said teasingly, 'He just hasn't done anything about it yet.'

Crystal turned away and Lucy's uncomfortable comment was lost in the confusion of unpacking the Kentucky Fried Chicken that the McGraws had brought with them. It turned into a warm evening, filled with laughter. Crystal learned that Max had an older son, David, who was out at a computer club meeting for the evening. Lucy was quieter in Max's company and Crystal could see that she enjoyed listening to her husband talking with Jesse.

The McGraws had a sail-boat and Crystal found herself promising to come sailing if she was in town long enough, regretting that she would probably have to fly back to Vancouver tomorrow. 'Mind you,' Lucy said, 'This is not the best time of year for sailing anyway. Cold and stormy. Next spring you could come and reasonably expect some sunshine. Jesse, you'll have to come too. Leave the seaplanes and play for a weekend.'

Crystal shook her head, but found she could not speak, could not look at Jesse. The evening was affecting her, watching Jesse play with Bonnie, watching him simply relaxing with his friends, being the man he had been for her out in the bushes. She had thought he would be a different person when he returned to the world, but he was the same Jesse.

She was going to miss him terribly. She looked down at her hands as Max and Lucy became involved in a technical conversation about the computer programming job they were doing. She wanted to wake up with Jesse near, to reach out and touch. She wanted to know that he was close, that he would come home to her.

She looked up and searched for him with her eyes, found him lying back lazily in his chair, enjoying a mild argument that Lucy and Max were having about which computer system would be best for the job they were working on. His eyes moved, drawn to Crystal, and she saw the warmth lighting them.

She loved him.

That had to be crazy, when they'd spent less than a week together, but she knew it was true, that it had been more than a week. It had been for ever, and she knew that he felt something for her, too. It was in his eyes, the gentleness of his hands touching. She took a slow, deep breath, not knowing what her eyes might have told him and suddenly frightened.

When the McGraws left, she would ask about Charlie.

If she tried, perhaps he would care more, perhaps she could convince him that she would not trap him, that she would not make demands like the woman he had almost married. She swallowed, remembering how they had made love, how she had hoped for a child. This man should have children. He was, as Lucy said, a natural family man. How would he react if she told him she was carrying his child?

Jesse got up to pour everyone a drink, handed hers with a softly spoken, 'Are you all right? You seem very thoughtful.'

'Yes,' she agreed huskily, aware of Lucy's curious eyes on them.

'Yes to which?' he asked, low-voiced, smiling.

'Both. I think I'm all right, and I am thoughtful.'

He bent and touched her lips with his, whispered, 'Later.'

'—think we should try it,' Lucy was saying eagerly.

'Easy, darling,' Max cautioned her. 'Sometimes I regret getting into payroll software. Everything's so subject to regulation. If I'd written a computer game, we could go off sailing and forget about annual updates.'

Jesse explained, 'Max wrote the SCS payroll software for computers.'

'I thought that was a Toronto company?'

'It was.' Max smiled at his wife and Crystal was surprised to see Lucy flush. 'SCS is based in Toronto, but

Lucy came out west, so I had to follow her.' He was smiling, saying, 'She took a little convincing before she agreed to let me stay.'

Lucy's colour was high as she said, 'He's a stubborn man.' Her eyes, though, were warm as they met her husband's, and Crystal wondered if she would ever know the story of Max and Lucy's romance.

To Max, she said, 'I did an audit on a company using your system last year. I was auditing income, not payroll, of course, but I had a look at the system. It's nice. Very easy to use.'

Lucy shifted higher, careful to avoid disturbing Bonnie whose head was in her lap. 'That's why I think Max should do an income tax system. He's got a knack for making the complicated seem simple when he writes a program.' She lifted a hand to still Max's protest. 'Darling, we've got a live tax expert here. We'll hire Crystal and get her to help draw up the specs, and she can work with us to——'

She felt panicky, Jesse's eyes on her. Her voice dropped. 'No, I—I'm not an expert. I'm very junior in the department.'

'Think about it,' said Lucy. It was lightly spoken, but Crystal half thought the words were serious. 'We could use someone who likes auditing in the firm. Personally, I'd rather work on computers, but I have a growing list of clients who need an audit at the end of their year.'

'You could move a lot of the audit procedures over to the computer,' volunteered Crystal, then she found herself in a vigorous discussion of audit software, then, somehow, in an argument with Jesse over his control systems.

'You'd better listen to her,' laughed Lucy.

He groaned. 'If you two accountants have your way, I won't be able to turn around without talking to a computer.' Crystal opened her mouth to protest and he leaned close to her, touching fingers to her lips and saying, 'All right, I'll agree. I'll give up.' She stared at him, not sure if he was serious. He said, 'Really. Do it, Lucy—Max. Whatever it takes.'

Lucy said, 'You're kidding?'

Max said, 'No, he isn't. It's just that Crystal is better than you at getting around his stubbornness.'

Jesse laughed and Crystal thought he was embarrassed, then she thought she must have imagined it.

'They're nice people,' she told him later as they stood together, watching the McGraws walk down the driveway, little Bonnie sleeping in her father's arms.

'Yes,' he agreed. Then he drew the door closed and turned her towards him. He stood in front of her in the empty house, saying softly, 'They're my best friends, but I spent the whole evening waiting for them to leave.'

She licked her lips, trembled as she felt Jesse watching the wet touch of her tongue on the dryness of her upper lip. 'Jesse——' He was waiting, not touching. 'I—I don't really know what you want from me.'

He bent and placed a fleeting kiss on her forehead. 'Do we have to decide that now?' he asked softly, his own voice ragged. 'Yesterday, before we got to Butedale, I thought we would say goodbye when we got back to civilisation.' His eyes were black fire, his fingers caressing the back of her arms. 'Now I don't know what I—I'm not ready for you to go yet.'

'Yet?' She swallowed. 'How long are you asking me for?'

He frowned and she knew he was feeling pressured. She should go home tomorrow, but she could tell her team manager that she needed a few days' sick leave first. She knew that she could stay, but should she?

What about Charlie?

Jesse's voice had faint tinges of impatience under the calm. 'Can't you just stall a few days? Tell your boss that there's things to attend to here. You have to put in a claim against me for what you lost. You should——'

'I don't want anything——'

'Don't be silly! You lost a computer, and I don't know what else was in that bag, and no one's seen any sign of the Cessna. Of course you're putting in a claim! I told you to make a list.'

She whispered, 'I don't want money from you.' She wanted love, his eyes lighting when she came near, his voice when she needed warmth, his loving in the nights.

Or did she? What if he loved her and held her in his arms, and then pushed her away? She would be more alone than ever before. What about Charlie? If Crystal stayed, would Charlie be pushed away?

Jesse pushed an unruly lock of hair back from his forehead, said, 'The insurance company will be paying.' He reached behind her and touched a switch, drowning the foyer in darkness, the only light a soft glow bathing them from above. He said softly into the darkness, 'I knew you were special the day you walked into my office. I looked up and—you knew it too, didn't you?'

She swallowed, staring at him and seeing only the darkness of his silhouette. She remembered how he had looked as she came through the doorway that first time, how for an instant he had been David.

'Crystal?' He took her hand. 'Tell me, honey? What was in your mind the first time you saw me?'

She shook her head. Her fingers tightened on his and he said, 'What's wrong? You're trembling!' His lips were close, because he knew how to warm her, to stop the trembling. She shivered despite his arms.

'This first time I saw you, I—I thought you were David.'

'David?' His voice was blank, startled. 'Max's son?' Then she felt the realisation hit him. 'David . . . your husband? Is that true?'

She nodded mutely, knowing that she had to finish it, to tell the rest and get it over with. 'There's more,' she whispered. 'Something else I have to tell you.'

He dropped his hands and she was alone. He was there, waiting, but he might have been a thousand miles away, a distant voice saying tightly, 'Then you had better tell me, hadn't you?'

Her mind cast about for something to tell him, anything to take that harshness from his voice, to have him touching her, warm and loving.

'Are we going to wait for ever for you to come out with it?' He was angry. She had not known what he would be like angry, but his voice was sharp, hard. 'What the hell do you mean, I look like David? How much like? Do you—when I was making love with you, did——'

'No!' She swallowed. 'Jesse, I—I don't know if you're going to understand this. I—I lied to you.'

'You lied——' He had not expected her to say that. She hurt inside, feeling his trust shatter. She had not realised until now that he had trusted her. 'How the hell could you lie to me? What—what lie?' She was silent and his voice went harder. 'Or was it all lies?'

She felt her fingers clenching, the nails digging into her palms, her voice flowing out of its own will. 'I told you—I said I couldn't have children. I—it wasn't true.'

She was glad of the dark, because she did not want to see his eyes right now. 'The accident?' he asked, his voice oddly hollow. 'You were hurt in the accident. You said you couldn't have children because of that.'

'I broke my arm. And I had cuts on my neck and scalp. That was all. Nothing—nothing else.' He was silent. She said on a whisper, 'I—it just happened, out there. That first night. Then after, I thought—I thought, what if there was a child? It—I wanted that.'

She thought she heard him swallow. 'What the hell do you mean? You wanted—you weren't going to tell me?' She was silent and he said raggedly, 'That's it, isn't it, Crystal? You wanted me to get you pregnant, so you could go home and have the kid by yourself. You wouldn't tell me. You weren't ever going to tell me, were you?'

It had been insanity, the kind of dream that turned into a nightmare. She said helplessly, 'I didn't think it would matter to you. I—you weren't supposed to know.'

The telephone pealed into the silence and he turned away from her, left her and went up the stairs, moving steadily, but not running as he had earlier in the evening. She followed him, coming to the top and watching his face as he picked up the receiver. Her words had destroyed whatever it was that he felt for her. His eyes hardly saw her now, and his lips were a tight bitterness.

'Hi,' he said gruffly to the telephone, then he listened. After a moment he said only, 'Yeah, OK. I'll come on down and have a look.'

He dropped the receiver and it hit with a bang, sliding off the cradle. He bent down carefully and replaced it. When he stood again, his face was cold with an anger she had never seen in him. She remembered Lucy's comment about Jesse's temper and she shivered.

'Jesse——'

'You know, I thought I was falling in love with you.' He laughed, but it was a terrible sound. She reached out a hand, but he ignored it. 'I've never let myself fall in love with anybody before, not like that. I think I would have done anything for you.' He shrugged as if it didn't matter, then said in a voice cold as the outdoors at night,

'I thought I knew everything about you, that you were closer to me than anyone had ever been.'

She was silent, horrified, watching, listening to laughter too harsh for Jesse. 'I really fell for it. I thought—damn you! When you told me you couldn't have kids, I hurt knowing how it hurt you. I wanted——'

She touched him and he jerked back as if he had been stung. 'No more lies,' he said tiredly. 'If you want a stud, go somewhere else. I'm not in the business. I thought you were a warm, grown-up woman, not a neurotic child trying to reconstruct the past.'

She shook her head blindly, but he did not seem to see. He picked up his jacket, started down the stairs, then stopped abruptly, looking back at her. For a second there was stillness. She thought he might listen now. If she could find the right words.

He said slowly, 'When we made love, was it David you—no! Don't answer that.' The muscles of his throat spasmed as he swallowed, then he turned away and there was only his harsh voice coming back at her, 'If there's a baby, it will be mine, you know. Not your husband's.'

'Jesse!' He was going, and she had a terrible feeling that he would never be back, not for her. 'Jesse, you don't understand! It wasn't like that! I didn't——' She heard the outside door jerked open. 'Jesse, where are you going?'

The slam of the door echoed through the night air, fading as she heard the angry sound of car tyres spitting gravel on the driveway.

CHAPTER NINE

CRYSTAL'S team manager handed her a new work list the day she returned to work. She started making client appointments for audits on northern Vancouver Island. She got a new audit-bag, and her new computer was requisitioned and delivered.

She had Murray up for dinner, then went down to his place for dinner a week later. They lived in the same building, had ever since he told her about the apartment vacancy three years ago. That was when she had decided to sell the house she had shared with David and Johnny, to be practical and move into a centrally located apartment.

But she had never felt so alone in her apartment before, never felt so isolated by a view of concrete buildings. Yet Jesse Campbell was disappearing from her life as if he had never been. For a while, there were ripples, echoes of the man.

She was contacted by the Ministry of Transport accident investigator, asked to describe the events of the crash. This, it seemed, was routine in any aircraft incident. Shortly after that she received a letter from Jesse's company with a cheque for her estimated losses and an itemised list which included the cost of the computer she had carried, plus compensation for her time lost, the insurance charges from the hospital, and an allowance for hotel and meals in Prince Rupert. The last item was ridiculous because Jesse had put her up in his house, and Lucy and Max had fed her dinner.

The letter was signed by Bruce Harlow, who she supposed must be the Bruce who had been in the office the day she had flown with Jesse. Included in the letter was a request that she send a list claiming her actual losses and advise them if the cheque was inadequate. Reading it, she wondered who had done such a thorough job of researching her losses. Someone had called the hospital to check the amount of her bill, contacted Revenue Canada to determine the value of her audit-bag and computer.

She sent the list immediately when she got the cheque. She was certain that without it Jesse would never get payment from his insurance company. The cheque must have come from Jesse himself, because no insurance company would pay damages without a claim for them. Although Bruce had written the letter, she sent the list addressed to Jesse, with a letter.

First she wrote him a letter telling him that she was sorry she had lied to him, that she would like to see him again, that her life felt empty without him. Then she tore it up and wrote a new letter thanking him impersonally and giving him her telephone number, *in case you have to contact me about anything else.*

Then, by some insanity, she almost signed it *love, Crystal*, but that was not true. She didn't want it to be true, because loving him seemed to hurt so much.

In the end she simply signed her name, sealed the letter and stamped it, then went out at midnight to find a postbox for it. That would have been the end of it, except that she found herself waiting, refusing Murray's invitation to go out to a new Mexican restaurant, sitting at home evenings and hoping the telephone would ring.

'You're getting worse,' Murray accused her.

He had come upstairs, unannounced, three days before she was due to go to Vancouver Island. He was sitting in her best living-room chair, sipping weak tea and glowering at her without talking much, the steam from the tea drifting up around his blond beard. Then, finally, he had exploded in a gentle tirade.

She turned away and went to the window. Why did she keep moving to windows these days, reaching towards the outdoors, the trees and the sounds? 'Murray, I'm OK. Just lay off and let me be. I just want things a little quieter, that's all.'

'I don't buy it.' She heard the chair creak as he sat up. 'Crystal, I know you, and I would have bet that an experience like that, walking out of the wilderness, surviving when all the odds were against it... If I had control of your fate, it's just what I would have ordered for you. It should have given you a new zest for life, brought you back ready to get out of your ridiculous rut and take some risks again!'

'Like loving?' she whispered, making the mistake of turning around to stare at him.

'Yes, exactly.' His eyes narrowed, the pale blue deepening as he seemed to find something in her face. 'The pilot? It has to be the pilot, doesn't it? Because there was no one else. Just you and him, out there, trying to survive.' She could see his slight smile starting, as if he were pleased to be proven right. 'What happened? You got scared? You ran away?' He saw her flaming face, read too much in her eyes and said quickly, 'You had an affair, out there in the wilderness. And then you ran away.'

'I—no, he—we had an argument.' That was not right, but even Murray was not close enough to talk to about the painful memories of Jesse. 'It's over, and I don't think I could have handled it anyway. I mean—a relationship.'

'So you're giving up?' Murray put his cup down with a slight bang.

'I don't want——'

'Of course you want. You're nuts about the guy.'

She shook her head. 'He has my telephone number. He could call.'

'I don't believe it!' He stood up and paced to the window. 'How many times have you told me that you're a modern woman? You like managing your own life, being in control?'

She looked bleakly around at her immaculate apartment. 'Haven't I proven it? I've got a career, a job. I——'

'And you're sitting here in Vancouver, pining away like a Victorian maiden, because the man you love isn't calling.'

'I didn't say I loved him.' She had tried to keep from saying it, again and again, in her mind.

'Don't you?' He got up and came across to her, glowering down at her. 'Listen, lady, it's time for you to come out and live again. Wake up those dreams and go for it. Make a set for the man. If you don't, you're going to regret it for the rest of your life.'

'Murray, please don't—— Is this all theory? Psychology? Something from your university courses? Or do you know?'

'From bitter experience, love. I let the lady of my life get away. She slipped right through my fingers and I didn't do a thing to stop her.' He grinned, said lightly, 'Now, if you're as much of an idiot as I was, we'll turn into two old fogies, sitting on our balconies and talking about what might have been.'

She could feel a trembling excitement growing inside her, and fear. 'Murray, I'd—if I tried, and it worked— he's a pilot. You hear about planes crashing all the time.

It is risky, flying in that country.' She swallowed, said huskily, 'I couldn't bear to have it all happen again, to lose someone I love.'

He didn't say anything for a long time, then he shrugged. 'Honey, living is risky. If you'd rather hide in your cave and be alone for the rest of your life, I guess you'd better just forget the man.'

Forget him. Alone for the rest of her life. Murray made it sound like a long time, and Jesse, in her dreams, seemed to call to her. Was she crazy? What did she know about him? That he was a good man to be stranded in the wilderness with. That she could walk with him for days, forgetting how the brambles hurt and her legs ached because they were talking and just enjoying what was supposed to be an ordeal of survival. That he spoke Spanish and laughed a lot. That his nephew came to him when there was trouble, and little Bonnie ran to him as if he were a special light in her life.

That was what he was, a special light, a man who made the bad things seem manageable, who made the pleasant things glow with life and joy. But when he had been reaching towards her she had lied to him. She knew that he had not forgiven that. If he had, he would have called her.

She bought an answering service for her telephone before she went to Vancouver Island. She recorded the message, wishing she could give a special message for him, but contenting herself with an impersonal, 'Hi! This is Crystal Selwyn. I'm out of town for a few days. If you leave a message at the sound of the beep, I'll call you when I get back.'

It rained all the time she was on the island. Winter coming. For the first time she found the lonely nights in a strange hotel depressing. Contrary to her usual custom of tidying up her papers on the last evening in the field, she checked out of the hotel in the evening and drove down the island in the night, taking the early ferry from Nanaimo to Horseshoe Bay on the mainland, dashing home and turning on her answering service.

'Hi, love! It's Mom. I didn't know you had one of those machines, but I think it's a super idea. Call me when you get back. I've got news for you.'

'Crystal, this is Alex. I just got back. I was wondering about dinner, but I guess you're out in the field. I'll catch you at work when you're back.' She frowned. Alex was a fellow auditor who had been away on a course for the last couple of months. Before he'd left, he had pursued her relentlessly. It looked as if he planned to resume his futile wooing of her now that he was back.

Nothing from Jesse. Nothing in the letterbox either. She called her mother and talked for half an hour, learned that her widowed parent was excitedly planning to go to Europe for a holiday with the man who had lived next door for fifteen years.

When she hung the phone up again, she felt the emptiness and called Murray at work to invite him for dinner.

'Sorry,' he said briskly, 'but I'm busy every night this week.'

'I thought on Saturday we could go for a hike up——'

'Nope. This new passion of yours for hiking through the wilds is too energetic for me. Why don't you fly up north for the weekend if you're at a loose end?'

He hung up and she was alone, making a face at the telephone and feeling her heart thundering hard. She had a long weekend coming up. Four days. If she did as Murray suggested, would Jesse want to see her? The place he had been filling in her life felt like a warm joy gone cold. More than anything, she wanted to hear his laughter again.

What if he would not talk to her, see her? She trembled, her hand hovering on the telephone, her impulse to call the travel agent wavering. What if she went to him and he brushed her off the way she had been brushing Alex off? She felt too wide open, too vulnerable. Crazy, because at first she had thought she wanted an affair, a child, but not a man. She must have been insane! No wonder he was so angry with her.

She booked the tickets and spent hours worrying, spending the next day at work, hovering over calling to cancel the flight. She arrived home to her lonely apartment after work, not knowing why she went to the telephone. To cancel the tickets, or to call Jesse?

It was Jesse's number she dialled, the digits embedded in her memory from one glance at his telephone a month ago. It rang five times. No answer. She knew she should hang up. He was out, not home. When she heard the click and the ring stopped, she felt sudden panic.

What was she going to say?

'Hi! Campbell residence.'

The voice was light and very female. It wasn't Lucy's voice. Of course not. Lucy lived next door. Crystal licked her lips and managed, 'Could I speak to Jesse, please?'

'Sorry. He's away for a week. Can I take a message for him?'

'No, I——' Who was this? 'Who are you?'

'This is Charlie. Sure you don't want to leave a message for Jesse? He'll be calling me tonight. If there's anything important——'

'No. I'll call back. Goodbye.'

She sounded like a nice girl. Too young for him, though. Damn it! What was a girl who sounded like she was barely out of her teens doing answering his telephone, saying Jesse would call her tonight?

She closed her eyes tight and tried to see the face of the blonde nurse. How young was she? Was Jesse—oh, damn! What did it matter? She would be crazy to start chasing a man who had a live-in woman already.

She called Murray. He sounded tired and a little distant. 'I thought you were flying north this weekend,' he said when she again suggested that they spend Saturday hiking around Lighthouse Park.

'Jesse's away, out of town.' She twisted the coiled wire of the telephone. 'A girl answered his telephone. Her name's Charlie. She had her shampoo in his bathroom, and she answers his telephone.' Her misery came through the words as she finished, 'I don't know where she sleeps. Will you please come Saturday?'

'I suppose so. Couldn't we do something less energetic?'

She thought of the trees, the incredible moment when Jesse had touched her, silencing her as they watched the black bear. Was she trying to reconstruct that dream? 'I'd just like to get outdoors and get some exercise. You could use it too.'

He sounded as if that had hit home, his voice coming back carrying faint resentment. 'All right, but only if you stop sounding like that Victorian maiden.'

'Murray, a girl answered the phone!'

He sighed. 'Crystal, believe it or not, sometimes a man and woman spend time together without there being any sexual significance. For example, how about you and me? Would you say we were romantically involved?'

She supposed some people thought they were, but the spark had never been there between them. It was one of the things that made him such a comfortable friend. 'Right,' he said, as if she had answered him. 'So what if I went away and you came down to water my plants. If the telephone rang, would you answer it?'

'Yes, but——' She closed her eyes. The receiver dug into her shoulder painfully. 'Are you suggesting I should chase after some macho character who is going to just play with me and then walk away to some other woman?' She frowned. The description did not sound like Jesse.

Murray's voice was sharp. 'You're being an idiot. If you fell in love with him, there's a lot more than that to the man; and it seems to me that you're the one who's been playing with him.'

The rest of the week dragged. Then, on Friday morning, her team manager handed out the next assignment.

'Prince Rupert,' he told her, grinning. 'You're bound for the north again, but this time do try to get up on time, Ms Selwyn. Don't miss the plane.'

She was too busy coping with her pounding heart to respond to the dig about sleeping in. It would be almost a month before they flew north, but meanwhile the team had work to do and Crystal tried to concentrate on it. She set to work making appointments, pushing back the real question. Next month, in Prince Rupert, would she call Jesse?

The third taxpayer she called referred her to his accountant, Lucy McGraw. She found her fingers trembling as she dialled the number and asked to speak to the accountant.

'Lucy, it's Crystal Selwyn. I'm calling from work. One of your clients has been selected for a routine tax audit.' She named the client and added, 'They've asked me to contact you to make arrangements.'

Amazingly, Lucy laughed. 'I never thought I'd look forward to a tax audit, but I'll be glad to see you. Maybe you can get Jesse out of his moodiness. When are you coming?'

Disorientated, she stared down at her engagement calendar. 'It's just in the arranging stages. There's a team coming up, six of us spread over the town. We'll be arriving December the second and staying until the eleventh.' Crystal's pencil hovered over the arrival date on her calendar. It would be exactly two months from the day she and Jesse walked down into Butedale.

'Super! I'll look forward to it. Now tell me what you want made ready for you. I haven't been involved in a tax audit before. Every piece of paper for how many years back?'

'The last four years.' Crystal described her requirements in detail.

'OK, I'll make sure it's ready—Max, hand me that pen, will you? Mine's run out—there. I've got it, Crystal. I'll have everything ready. Will you stay with us? We'd love to have you. Or are you staying with Jesse?'

Crystal jerked a harsh black line through the page on her engagement calendar. She dropped the pen before it did more damage. 'Thanks, Lucy, I—I'd love to, but I can't stay with you when I'm auditing one of your clients.'

Lucy understood instantly. 'Sorry, I didn't think of the auditor's objectivity and all that. OK, we'll make it another time. Meanwhile, I'll clear the decks so I can be available for you when you come to do the audit. I expect you'll be at Jesse's anyway, won't you? How far does objectivity go? Do we avoid dropping over evenings to see you?'

'I—Jesse doesn't know. I—I haven't talked to him since—— ' Since he walked out that night, leaving her alone in his house. '—since I left.'

'So that's why he's been so difficult.' There was a confused silence, then, 'Sorry, Crystal. I didn't mean to pry. I thought—— He's out of town right now, gone to buy a new plane to replace the one that he lost. He's flying it out from back east.' She was talking quickly, trying to cover her confusion. 'We're all filling in for him, feeding the girls.'

She might never have a better chance. She felt her mouth go dry and she thought Lucy must notice how her words struggled to get out. 'What about Charlie?'

'She's on evening shift at the hospital again, so I've been doing the night feedings. Charlie does the mornings. The girls manage to make us both believe that the last feeding was missed, but we check with each other, so they're not putting anything over on us.'

She almost accepted Lucy's answer, but Murray's voice was somewhere there in her subconscious, telling her what a coward she was, a Victorian maiden. 'Lucy, I didn't mean about the cats. I was wondering about Charlie—I——'

'Oh, she's fine. The usual, you know.' She laughed and said warmly, 'Lord, Jesse has so much trouble with his brother's kids. I didn't realise you were into all the details of Jesse's family. The problem children, I call them. Charlie's getting over her miseries. She's got a new boy on the string, and ecstasy is growing again. That girl could use some growing up and settling down.' Lucy giggled and said, 'Max is laughing at me. He says I'm not one to talk about settling down. I've been here four years, and that's the longest I've lived anywhere in my entire life. Anyway, you don't want to hear about me. You'll want to know about Keith, too, I suppose.'

Crystal's head was spinning, trying to keep up with Lucy's chatter. '. . . gone with Jesse. They had a blow-up at home, so Jesse talked them into letting him out of school for a week. Personally I think Jesse's brother causes the whole problem. He's too darned strict with those kids, and Diane has no sense of humour, so they end up running to Jesse. He's done more to bring them up than either Harvey or Diane. He was the one who talked Charlie into going into nurse's training, and he'll be the one to straighten Keith out.'

Crystal found the pen in her hand again. It was moving on its own, doodling a happy face on the inside cover of the taxpayer file.

'And Jesse?' she asked, her voice suddenly dropping to a whisper. 'How is Jesse himself?'

Papers rustled and Lucy sounded suddenly closer to the telephone. 'As I said, Crystal, Jesse Campbell has been as irritable and moody as hell ever since you left town, so I hope you're serious about the man.'

Was she? She was frightened, she knew that, perhaps even as frightened as she had been on that fishing net, climbing up to Jesse. She was not sure if she was glad or sorry that there was no way to contact Jesse right now. Was Lucy right? Was Jesse upset over her? If so, it didn't mean that he had forgiven her for lying to him.

She took work home every night that week, and on Saturday she wore Murray out hiking through the park.

'Come up for coffee?' she urged him afterwards. They were in the lift, almost home, and she didn't want to be alone. She pushed the button for her floor.

'You know, you have a problem.' He was leaning back against the side of the elevator, his pale blue eyes a little too penetrating. 'You're avoiding being alone. If you're going to live alone, you'd better——'

'Stop being a psychologist!' she snapped. 'Do you want to come up for coffee or not? You paid for the supper, I figure I owe you a cup of coffee at least.' She pushed her hands into her jeans pockets, stretching the stiff fabric.

He rolled his eyes. 'The woman has an adding machine for a mind. Now I'm an item on your personal balance sheet. I owe, you owe—all right, but make it tea. I can't take any more coffee. That waitress was far too quick with the refills.'

Murray stepped out of the elevator ahead of her, turning to wait for her. 'Come on, lazybones. You ate too much, you know. That's the trouble with taking you to a smorgasbord. You don't know when to stop.'

'And you do?' She let her eyes drop to his midsection. 'I think you're starting a bit of a pot belly, my dear.' She laughed as she saw him quickly suck in his stomach. 'That got you where it hurts, didn't——'

She saw him then. A tall man, dark and quiet. He had been leaning against the wall near her door, a newspaper in his hand. Waiting. Jesse. Her feet moved her, brought her closer, and he just stood there, waiting for something. She stopped when she could almost touch him.

She had forgotten all about Murray until his low voice prompted her, 'Introductions, Crystal.'

She swallowed, whispered, 'Jesse.' He still didn't say anything. She managed, 'Murray, this is Jesse. Jesse... Murray.' Jesse nodded. She didn't know if he was ever going to talk. He looked angry. She had hoped the anger would be over.

'I'm on my way,' said Murray, his eyes locked with Jesse's. Neither man was smiling. Crystal could feel crackling in the air around them, as if messages were being sent and received without her hearing them. 'I'll be downstairs, Crystal.'

She nodded numbly, wanting Murray to go, yet afraid of being alone with this frowning Jesse. Walking away, Murray paused and turned back. 'Crystal, don't forget what I said. You've got to——'

'Murray!' My God! The man was insane! Was he going to tell her again to stop behaving like a Victorian maiden? In front of Jesse? 'Murray, please get out of here!'

He grinned then, said, 'Public corridor, my dear. Goodbye, Jesse. Crystal isn't good at introductions, is she? Perhaps we'll meet again.'

When he was gone, she was tremblingly alone with Jesse. She knew now what Lucy meant when she said he was moody these days. She fumbled with her bag, her fingers closing over her keys. Jesse shifted, his eyes following the empty corridor where Murray had been.

'What did he say?'

'What?' she echoed stupidly.

'He told you not to forget something. Something you have to do.' She saw a muscle work in his jaw.

'He—he—I can't possibly tell you about it.' His eyes jerked to her and she found that he was angry, the black blazing into her wide, vulnerable eyes.

'What kind of a relationship is it that you have with him? You sounded—he knows about me?' She nodded and he said, 'What does he know?'

She licked her lips, looked down at the keys, 'I——' Murray knew that she loved Jesse. She had not told him exactly, but he knew.

'Crystal, if you wanted a baby, why didn't you—is he your lover?' The harsh words echoed through the corridor. Somewhere a door clicked. Jesse's eyes flickered behind her.

'Why are you here?' she asked painfully. This was terrible, his eyes so hard and angry. What was he doing here if he didn't care about her? Why didn't he leave her alone?

He took the keys from her numb fingers, spread them and selected one. It was the wrong one. The lock refused it. The second one he tried was right and the door swung open, stopping with a faint thud against the rubber stopper. She went past him, through her own doorway, not looking at him.

He closed the door. She unzipped her jacket and he took it from her, and she managed all the while not to look at him, to walk away towards her small kitchenette, saying dully, 'I'll get you some coffee.'

She found the electric kettle where she had left it that morning, filled it with water and plugged it in.

'I don't want coffee,' he said angrily.

She could see his shadow blocking the light from the living-room and she was terrified that he would not stay, that there was something terrible he wanted to say, something angry and hurtful, and that he would go when it was said.

'Tea, then.' The kettle was on, anyway. She reached for the canister that held her teabags.

'I'm not Murray. He drinks tea, doesn't he?'

She nodded. Eventually she would have to look at him.

'Why didn't you tell me he was your lover?'

She looked and he had the anger hidden. His eyes were an impersonal black, his mouth void of expression as he said cruelly, 'If I were Murray, I wouldn't walk away and leave you alone with me. He lives here, doesn't he?'

'No.' She wasn't sure why he was asking. There was no loving in his eyes. 'He lives in an apartment downstairs. And I told you before, Murray's my friend. We're not lovers.'

'I know what you said, but you lied to me.'

'Only once,' she whispered painfully, turning away. The kettle was boiling and she didn't know what to do with it. She didn't want coffee either, and she kept the tea mainly for Murray. She didn't care for it. 'What can I offer you?' she asked desperately. 'Some huckle-berries?' He pulled the kettle's plug out of the wall, but he didn't answer.

'Jesse, why are you here?' She made herself look at him. He was pushing the dark hair back with one hand. He looked uncomfortable.

'I came to find out if I'm going to be a father. I need to know if your little plan came to pass. Are you pregnant, Crystal?'

'Oh, God!' She hugged herself with both arms. Lucy had said he was moody, but it didn't mean that he missed her. He was upset because he thought he had unwittingly fathered a child.

'Are you?'

She shook her head, staring at the V-neck of the sweater he wore under his open jacket. The sweater was soft and fitted him in a way that showed all the hard muscles without being too obvious about it. She wondered if he knew how good it made him look.

His hand moved and she knew the fingers were coming to touch the underside of her chin, to lift her eyes up to his. She didn't know what he saw. She felt numb, not unlike the feeling she had had as she clung to the log out in the water after the crash.

'I need words, Crystal.' His voice had softened. He sounded as he might if he were talking to young Bonnie, or perhaps even Keith. 'This is a little too important for a nod and a misunderstanding. Is—are you carrying my child?'

She shook her head again. 'No. No, Jesse. I'm not pregnant.'

'You're sure?'

'Yes.' It hurt her to see the relief in his eyes. She pulled away, going back to the kettle. 'I'm having coffee.' She would be up all night, but it didn't matter. She wasn't going to sleep anyway. 'If you don't want any—if that's all you came for, I——' She bit her lip, staring at the coffee grounds in the canister. The filter first. She had to put the filter in, then the grounds. She didn't want him to leave. She didn't know what to say to him, but she didn't want him to walk out of the door. She stared at the kettle and said slowly, 'I'm sorry I lied to you. I was sorry the minute I'd done it, but——' It had been done then, and she had wanted his arms around her.

He stepped back from her, found a kitchen chair and straddled it, facing her, looking still too serious for Jesse. He wasn't going yet. She swallowed and tried to think of something to say, to keep him.

'How's Keith? I thought he was with you. I thought you were flying a plane back.'

'How did you know that?' The chair scraped on the floor. It would be a black mark, hard to clean.

'I called Lucy.' She watched herself knock the canister over, the coffee grounds flowing all over the counter. 'I'm doing an audit up there next month, and she's the accountant. She told me you were away with Keith, getting a new plane.'

He pushed his hand through his hair again. He seemed oddly uneasy, not like the Jesse she thought she knew. Why was he so nervous? Was it relief, because she was not having his child? What was keeping him here?

'What about some lemonade, or pop or something?' he asked abruptly. 'I don't want coffee, but if you've got something else——'

'A cider? Or a beer?'

'The beer. Yes, please.' He watched her going to the refrigerator. 'I thought you might have called the house.' She opened the beer and took down a glass from the cupboard. 'No glass,' he said. 'I'll just have the bottle.'

She handed it to him. She had to think of things to say, or he would go. What man wanted to try to talk to...to a Victorian maiden afraid of her own desires?

'Charlie said a woman called.'

She went back to the refrigerator and took out a cider for herself, poured the cool liquid into a glass. 'There are a lot of women around you. It could have been anyone.'

'It wasn't Lucy. Charlie would have recognised her voice. And there aren't that many women around me.'

'Aren't there?' She didn't know what to do with her eyes. She curled her hands around the glass and sipped, but her eyes kept going to him. She wished he would smile, laugh. She wished she knew why he was here. 'I thought there were women everywhere around you.'

'No.' He wasn't drinking the beer, just holding it. 'I haven't had a lot of time for relationships.'

'You travel too much. You told me.' Was this why he was staying, to be sure she understood there was no room in his life for her?

'Yes,' he agreed. 'Of course, there have been women, but—no one who mattered enough for me to start changing my life.'

'You're happy with your life.' She had seen that. 'You like flying, and you like the business of being in business. And at home you've a full life. Everyone comes to you, Charlie and Keith and Bonnie. And you like that.' She would have liked to share it, but he had said no one mattered enough. She bit her lip, said, 'I do understand that, Jesse. I know you're not looking for——'

'I wasn't.'

His words lay between them like a silent explosive. She put her glass down on the counter. If she didn't, it was going to break. Murray, she thought desperately, I really don't know how to do this. I'm afraid.

He said, 'I'm here until Tuesday. The plane needs some adjustments. It won't be ready to fly on until then. I— Keith's with me, but—I wondered if we could go out to lunch. The three of us, if you like. Tomorrow?'

'Yes.'

Her acceptance seemed to hang between them. He said, 'All right. I——' He reached across and put the beer down on the counter. 'I guess I'd better go, then.'

He left, and she was torn between anticipation and uncertainty. What did he want from her?

CHAPTER TEN

HE KNEW he was making a mess of it, but he didn't know how he should go about courting Crystal Selwyn and he was terrified of losing her.

He had called directory enquiries for her telephone number the day she left Prince Rupert, but he had never used it. He'd be crazy, wouldn't he, to pursue a woman who was so unwilling to love him that she would trick him into fathering her child—so that she could be a mother and not his wife?

Wife. He hadn't thought of marriage until then, but the thought came to him as if he had known it was right all along. They belonged together, for ever. Yet no sooner did that certainty come over him than he pushed it away with the panic of a man who had been too long a bachelor.

So he worked, spent evenings sitting in his own chair and remembering Crystal sitting there with Tabby in her lap. At work, whenever he flew over Princess Royal Island he felt as if someone were tearing him apart.

Lucy kept asking about Crystal. He could not remember her asking after any of the other women he dated. Keith asked too, as if he knew Crystal was special.

Then she wrote with her list of losses from the accident. She dropped her telephone number on to the page of that stiff business letter so casually that he was afraid she meant nothing by it. Simply, *in case you have to contact me about anything else.*

Did anything else include loving her?

Was she expecting his child? He would have to find out soon, but he had trouble with the thought of facing her, asking about a child she did not want him to know about. How the hell had it happened? How could a man go from thinking he was perfectly happy with his busy life to finding his nights and evenings empty, his days filled with empty moments when he ached to pick up a telephone and hear her voice?

He leapt at the arrangements for the new Cessna. He would take delivery personally, fly it back himself. He would break the journey in Vancouver and go to see her. What if she were expecting his child? That would be a serious complication. If there were a child, he would ask her to marry him. He would have to do that, then somehow hope that it would work out, that in the end he would have a wife loving him, not tied to him for the child's sake.

He phoned home from the Calgary airport, got Charlie on one of her nights off and was shaken to learn that a woman had called him. A woman who would not leave her name. It had to be Crystal, but why would she call? To say that there was a child? To talk to him about their child?

The wishful dreamer in him volunteered, to say she loves you, but he hardly dared hope for that.

In Vancouver, he called and her recorded voice answered. He felt like a trembling adolescent, afraid to ask a girl for a date. He didn't leave a message. He took Keith downtown to look at all the computer stores, then abruptly decided that he could not wait and left Keith, after arranging to meet him later. Then he got someone to buzz him into Crystal's building, took the lift to her apartment and waited until she came.

When he saw her, he wanted to run to her, take her into his arms and never let her go. But she was not alone, and she did not seem happy to see him.

He had been sick with relief when she said she was not pregnant, then regret had surged over him. He wanted to touch her, to make love to her, to feel her swelling belly and know that a life was growing, a life they had created together. He wanted to reach out and stop her playing with the kettle, to take her in his arms and tell her everything he was feeling. He didn't do any of that. He was so nervous, afraid, that he had included his nephew in the invitation to lunch, for God's sake!

Yet the next day he was glad that he had brought Keith. She sounded nervous when he buzzed her from the foyer, but when she opened the door, she saw Keith and smiled, opening the door wider and inviting them both in.

'I'll just be a minute. Keith, there's a bowl of taco chips on the table in the living-room. Help yourself.' She grinned at Jesse and he felt his heart hammer through his ribcage. 'You too, Jesse.'

Keith was a walking perpetual appetite. He cleaned up the crisps enthusiastically while Jesse waited nervously. Then she joined them, standing beside him, looking out the window and smiling. 'It's not like your view, is it?'

'Not much.' He grinned at her, then asked, 'Which do you prefer?' his pulse going wild when her eyes flared green.

'Yours. Your view is much nicer than mine.'

Then they had left, and he told himself to be patient. She was talking about the view, just the view, but he felt excited and immeasurably happy.

They went to Stanley Park, had lunch at the Pavilion before they went to see the bears and the monkeys. Later, as the afternoon deepened towards evening, they took a long walk along the sea wall, looking out to the ocean. 'It's so much tamer,' she told him with a laugh. 'I really don't expect to be attacked by a bear, or to have to climb up a fishing net to a cliff.'

He was silent, wanting to say that he would like to take her back there, to the place where she had first been his. Keith swung around and asked her, 'Was it terrible? Were you afraid?'

'Sometimes.' She was very still. Jesse could feel her stillness, although he was not facing her. Then he turned and found her eyes watching him, very deep and brown. Her eyes changed with her emotions, the hazel going green when she was frightened or angry, brown when he made love to her.

'Sometimes I was terrified,' she was saying slowly. 'But sometimes... It was the most marvellous experience of my life. It——' She spread her hands in a formless gesture. 'Words make it seem commonplace. It was more than any words could describe.'

If she was talking to Keith, her eyes were not where her words were going. Jesse swallowed, then found himself asking painfully, 'Would you do it again? Go out there again? Deliberately?' With me? his eyes asked.

Her eyes dropped away from his in confusion, then lifted. They were green now, laughing and something else as she said softly, 'Is that an invitation?'

The sun was setting behind them, the sky turning red and black. He decided that it was time to stop being a coward and make his move. He said, 'Keith, you don't mind spending the evening watching television in our hotel, do you? I'm taking Crystal dancing.'

She broke her shampoo bottle, knocking it on to the floor of her bathroom while she was showering. Then she cut her finger cleaning it up. Until then she had thought she had lots of time to bath and shampoo and try to make herself as feminine and attractive as she could.

Her hair was finally done, dry and softly curling around her face, a soft curtain to her shoulders. Would he like it like that? Or should she tame it a little, pin it back and make herself look a little more sophisticated?

She hesitated, but her hands were trembling and she was afraid she would make a mess of trying a more complicated hairstyle. She hoped she would be what he wanted. Surely, if he had liked her out in the bushes, with her clothes in tatters and her hair caked with salt water, she would be all right like this?

She had never been so nervous of a date before. She tried to remember how it had been with David, but it was so long ago and she had been so much younger, a different person. She was certain there had never been this delicious fear.

Delicious fear. She grinned at her image in the mirror. How many times had she been terrified in the days after the Cessna went down and left them stranded? If he took her somewhere wild and lonely, flew her away from the world, she thought she might be able to stand a little more confident in front of him, perhaps even to be the woman Murray thought she should be, reaching and asking for what she was afraid to want.

The downstairs buzzer rang while she was hovering between the green dress and the amber. She rushed to the intercom, said, 'Come on up. Here's the buzzer.' Then she pressed it and she heard the click that told her he had opened it and was on his way up.

She unlocked the front door and flew back into her bedroom in her panties and bra. Which? The green did things for her eyes, but the amber brought out the lights in her hair. She heard the lift and pulled on the amber.

'Come in!' she called when he knocked. Oh, lord! She could feel his presence. Just the sound of the door opening and closing, and she knew he was close. She twisted to get at the zipper, slid it half-way up before it jammed. 'I'll just be a minute,' she gasped. 'Help yourself to something from the refrigerator if you like!'

'I'm fine.' He sounded it, his voice deep and warm and very close. She tried reaching back from up above, grasping the tab to the zipper, but it seemed to be hopelessly jammed.

She heard the door to her balcony slide open. He was out on the balcony, looking at the city lights and waiting for her. She would have to go for the green, after all, because this zipper was never going to go the rest of the way up.

Or down, it seemed. She twisted, but the dress would not come off. The zip had closed willingly over the narrowness of her waist, and there was no way the material would stretch, either up or down. She wrestled with it, but it was useless. She was stuck, and not quite dressed! She opened the door a crack, silently. He was out there, his back to her. He was dressed in a suit, looking very sleek and city. Sophisticated, yet she knew that under it all was the man who had led her out of the wilderness.

She hesitated. Murray would point out that her position was a hopeless one for a Victorian maiden. She could not possibly ask a man to come and help with such an intimate problem. She would be trapped in here for ever, or reduced to some idiocy like calling for help on the bedroom extension of her telephone.

Well, she was no maiden, for heaven's sake! Jesse would laugh at that after the way she had behaved out there in the wilderness. She was a grown woman, and that was a grown man out there. And she loved him.

She stepped out of the bedroom and let the door close behind her, leaning against it, hoping for some kind of courage from the wood. He had heard and turned towards her. He was stepping through the doorway, sliding the patio door closed behind him.

There was an instant when neither of them seemed to be able to speak. Jesse recovered first. 'You look lovely.'

'So do you,' she whispered, and she saw the laughter breaking on his face.

'That wasn't quite the effect I was trying for.' He looked down at himself, the dark suit, the shining leather shoes. He had slipped open the buttons of the jacket, revealing a silk shirt that she had a wanton urge to explore with her fingers. When he spoke, she could hear the lovely laughter just under his voice. 'Do you want to slip your shoes on? I think I've found a good place for dancing. I hadn't thought about it's being Sunday night, but the desk clerk at the hotel seemed to think that wouldn't be a problem. I——'

'I've got a bit of a problem with my zipper.' She smoothed the frothy skirt down with her hands, stared at her nylon-covered feet. 'It's stuck. I wondered if you could get it loose for me?'

She watched him walking towards her, wondering if he was feeling what she felt. She hoped he would forget the zipper, draw her close and cover her lips. If he did, then she knew that he would take her to the place where her dreams always led her these days.

'Turn around,' he said gently, his hands moving her, then his fingers going to the small of her back. She felt his touch on the flesh above the open zipper and tried not to tremble. His hands were moving, but the zipper wasn't. She twisted to see.

'Stop moving about!' His voice was sharp, then quickly soft, 'This is bloody impossible. I——' She felt the fingers on her bare shoulders. She turned and found his lips close and hers parted, an invitation he did not refuse.

It was like coming home, but more. The spinning of paradise and the comfort of home, the two mixed until she gasped as his hands slid across her bare back. Then there was only the spinning.

His hair was wonderfully soft and curling around her fingers, his lips firm yet hot against hers. She shuddered and felt her curves mould against his hardness.

'I knew it was impossible,' he groaned, chuckling. He drew his lips away from hers slowly. She found her head tipped back, resting against his arm, her eyes hardly able to open and see his frowning face.

'Didn't you want that?' she whispered, Murray's Victorian maiden forgotten. She could feel his hands against her back, could see deep into the blackness of his eyes. She thought she could see all the way into his soul, and she knew that he must see everything that was boiling inside her.

'Of course I want it.' His hands slid down her back, slipped over the fabric and settled on her hips. 'I've wanted it ever since I came through that door, long before that . . . always. But, honey, I really was going to try to fix your zipper. If you hadn't wiggled and sent my blood pressure soaring——' She felt him shrug, then his lips brushed the soft curling hair away from her forehead so that he could explore the white skin there.

She closed her eyes, admitted, 'If you do much more of that, I might not be able to stand up.' His hands moved, sliding down to cup her buttocks.

'I won't let you fall,' he whispered, that wonderful laughter mixed with the huskiness of him.

'Your blood pressure——' Those words penetrated finally and she frowned, worried. 'Do you have trouble with your blood pressure?'

'Not until I met you.' He found the tender lobe of her left ear and drew it into his mouth. She shivered as he dropped his lips to the smooth expanse of her neck, then she could bear no more and she twisted in his arms, her mouth searching his, giving up what his lips and his tongue probed for. When he lifted his head there was a long moment where even the sounds of the traffic outside were stilled.

'You're never going to believe this,' he said finally, his breath uneven when he tried to get words out, 'but I wasn't going to make love to you tonight.'

She had not thought it would be possible to be cold in his arms, but his words frightened her. If he walked away, she might be alone for ever. 'Why?' she asked finally. 'Why weren't you going to make love to me?'

He was the one that pulled away then, turning away, going to the window. She recognised it as Jesse's inevitable instinct, to move towards the outdoors, away from the buildings and towards nature. But there was nothing for him outside her patio doors, only city and traffic. He swung back, but kept his distance.

'It was going to be different.' He pushed a restless hand through his hair. 'I was going to start at the beginning.'

Confused, she asked, 'What do you mean? Where is the beginning?'

'Wherever you want it to be.' He paced across her floor. He needed a bigger room than this. Two strides and he was at her front door, three more and he was back close to her and she could feel the restlessness in him. 'Everything happened too quickly. It——' He shook his head, seeming to hear his own words. 'No, not too quickly. It was ... perfect. At least, I thought it was.'

He was frowning again, but she could see his eyes and, amazingly, he was nervous. She touched his cheek, felt a muscle twitch under her fingers. She whispered, 'I thought it was perfect, too. But afterwards, I was afraid.'

He didn't kiss her, but she felt as if he had. His hands took gentle possession of her face, fingers curving around into her hair. He said unevenly, 'I wanted to give us both time, to let things happen between us. We had all the extremes, bears and ravines and the crash ... making spectacular love. I thought we should fill in some of the gaps, and see what happens.'

She could see it in his eyes, hear it in his voice. He loved her. He might not be ready to say it, even to himself, but it was there. She wasn't sure where it would lead, because he had said he was not a marrying man, and she knew she wanted everything from him. But most of all she wanted to love him. She slipped her arms up around his shoulders, drawing him closer, inviting his kiss and much more.

He said, 'I thought of taking you up in the plane. I didn't know if you would be afraid to fly after that crash.'

'I'm not afraid.' She would trust him with her life. After all, he had proven worthy of her trust more than once. 'Where were you going to take me in the plane?'

'Somewhere away from all this.' He didn't move, but he was indicating the city, the buildings, and the traffic. 'I was hoping that you didn't need this, that we could go somewhere—I thought if I landed somewhere far away, where there was no one but us, then I could tell you....'

He trembled when she touched him, and her own fear was draining away. 'What were you going to tell me?'

He evaded her question, said, 'That was what I was going to do when I came here, try to get you to come flying with me—then Keith turned up with another crisis, and I thought it was just as well I had to bring him.'

Her heart crashed and she stopped breathing as his fingers tightened against her face. 'I don't think either of us needs to be shown that we can make a go of it together out in the bushes.' His eyes were uncertain. 'It's the rest of our lives. I thought—I decided I'd better try to appeal to the rational side of you. I'd try to convince you to come up north, to visit me.'

She said weakly, 'Are you asking me now?'

He nodded. 'You're coming, aren't you? Next month, you said? I'm not sure if I can wait that long, but I could come down on the weekends, fly down and if you weren't too busy we could see each other.'

She said yes, but he did not seem to hear. 'Then, when you come up north—do you have to stay at a hotel? You could stay at my place. If you—I'm not asking you to sleep with me, only if you want to.' He grinned then, admitted, 'God! I hope you want to. If not, you could have Charlie's apartment downstairs. I'd like you to stay there, in my house, because I'm hoping you'll live there with me one day.'

Yes. She opened her lips, but all she could manage was, 'What about Charlie?'

'She can stay with her parents while you're there. It's time she made up the fight anyway. Harvey's been ridiculous with those kids ever since they hit their teens, but Charlie's a grown woman now, or she should be, and she should start spending a little time straightening out her relationship with her parents.'

She touched his lips with hers. Soon he would make love to her, would pick her up and carry her into her bedroom. Somehow he would get this dress off. She smiled a little, because she really didn't care if he ripped it, even though it was one of her favourites.

'Jesse, you don't need to kick Charlie out for me.' She trembled and knew that he felt it. 'I don't want to stay in Charlie's apartment. I want to be with you.'

He swallowed and she knew that he was holding back, that he wanted badly to take her in his arms. She moved against him, knowing she was making it harder and feeling the knowledge fill her with a wild desire for him.

'She'll have to go anyway, sooner or later.' He was having trouble speaking and she pressed closer, so that his hands slipped around her and brought her hard against him.

Then his lips covered hers and she couldn't speak at all for a long moment, until he lifted his head and she managed to whisper, 'Please, Jesse...please stop talking and take me into the bedroom and somehow get this dress off me.'

'Honey,' it was a groan against her throat, 'I truly didn't intend this. I—I was going to be careful, take it very slowly. I'm not prepared for it, and I don't want there to be a baby.' He took her lips with his again, he could not stay away from her sweetness. 'First I wanted there to be just you and me. Alone. Later there will be our children. I want there to be, but first just us.'

She stopped his words with a shuddering kiss that left them both shaken. 'It's all right,' she said softly. 'There won't be a child.' Something flashed in his eyes and she said, 'It's true this time, I promise. I went to the doctor. I can give you her name if you want. You can call her.'

He was very still, and she thought her heart had stopped. Once she had lied to him. Could he trust her now? 'Jesse, it's true. I did go to the doctor.'

'I believe you, honey.' He touched her face gently. 'I never expected to love anyone like this. I love you so

much it scares me. I want to reach out and touch you,
to have every minute of you that I can. I want to know
where you are, to be able to call you and say hello when
I'm in the middle of the day and suddenly you're there,
in my heart, drowning out everything else.'

She drew his lips down to hers and he lifted her in his
arms because neither of them could wait any longer. As
he laid her down on her bed he said softly, 'You're going
to have to tell me if I'm going too fast, if I'm asking
too much. I'm not going to mess up your life, honey. I
swear I won't. Even if you want to stay down here,
working, somehow we'll manage it. I——'

'I want it all,' she said as he touched the zipper and
it slid down along the fabric for him. 'I love you, and
I want everything. I want to live with you, in your house.
Your children. My job—I'll find something up there.'
With Lucy and Max, perhaps. If not, there would be
something else.

He slid the fabric down, away from her shoulders. He
stared down at the lacy bra, then his eyes found hers.
'You wear the sexiest underwear,' he said softly. 'Do
your clients know what's underneath when you do an
audit?'

'We call them taxpayers, not clients. And no, they
don't know.'

She laughed and he said, 'That's good. I want it to
be just for me... everything... always. I love you and I
want you to marry me, and I want it for ever.'

'Yes,' she promised.

Looking down at her lovely face, he said softly, 'And
I don't believe that you were thinking about another man
when we made love.'

'I'm glad,' she whispered, 'because there was only you.
There's never been anyone I've loved this way. Just you.'

Then she reached up and kissed his lips, closing her eyes as he touched her and made her his, and the dreams flowed over them and through them...and became reality.

UNSTOPPABLE ROMANCE

Folly to Love
LYNN JACOBS

Take Away the Pride
EMMA RICHMOND

A Question of Trust
SHIRLEY KEMP

Designed with Love
KATHRYN ROSS

Mills & Boon are proud to present their
1989 NEW AUTHOR SELECTION

The selection features four brand new novels from some of our latest authors. Varied storylines guarantee a strong mix of love, drama and sparkling entertainment which proves that romance is unstoppable!

Price: £5.00   Published: April 1989

Available from Boots, Martins, John Menzies, W.H. Smith, Woolworths and other paperback stockists.

THE COMPELLING AND UNFORGETTABLE SAGA OF THE CALVERT FAMILY

April	August	November
£2.95	£3.50	£3.50

From the American Civil War to the outbreak of World War I, this sweeping historical romance trilogy depicts three generations of the formidable and captivating Calvert women – Sarah, Elizabeth and Catherine.

The ravages of war, the continued divide of North and South, success and failure, drive them all to discover an inner strength which proves they are true Calverts.

Top author Maura Seger weaves passion, pride, ambition and love into each story, to create a set of magnificent and unforgettable novels.

W●RLDWIDE

Widely available on dates shown from Boots, Martins, John Menzies, W.H. Smith, Woolworths and other paperback stockists.

AROUND THE WORLD WORDSEARCH
COMPETITION!

How would you like a years supply of Mills & Boon Romances ABSOLUTELY FREE? Well, you can win them! All you have to do is complete the word puzzle below and send it in to us by October 31st. 1989. The first 5 correct entries picked out of the bag after that date will win **a years supply of Mills & Boon Romances** (*ten books every month - **worth around £150***) What could be easier?

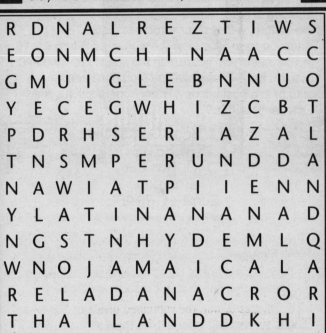

```
R D N A L R E Z T I W S
E O N M C H I N A A C C
G M U I G L E B N N U O
Y E C E G W H I Z C B T
P D R H S E R I A Z A L
T N S M P E R U N D D A
N A W I A T P I I E N N
Y L A T I N A N A N A D
N G S T N H Y D E M L Q
W N O J A M A I C A L A
R E L A D A N A C R O R
T H A I L A N D D K H I
```

ITALY	THAILAND	SCOTLAND	SWITZERLAND
GERMANY	IRAQ	JAMAICA	
HOLLAND	ZAIRE	TANZANIA	
BELGIUM	TAIWAN	PERU	
EGYPT	CANADA	SPAIN	
CHINA	INDIA	DENMARK	
NIGERIA	ENGLAND	CUBA	

PLEASE TURN OVER FOR DETAILS ON HOW TO ENTER ➡

HOW TO ENTER

All the words listed overleaf, below the word puzzle, are hidden in the grid. You can find them by reading the letters forward, backwards, up or down, or diagonally. When you find a word, circle it or put a line through it, the remaining letters (which you can read from left to right, from the top of the puzzle through to the bottom) will spell a secret message.

After you have filled in all the words, don't forget to fill in your name and address in the space provided and pop this page in an envelope (you don't need a stamp) and post it today. Hurry - competition ends October 31st. 1989.

Mills & Boon Competition,
FREEPOST,
P.O. Box 236,
Croydon,
Surrey. CR9 9EL
Only one entry per household

Secret Message _____

_____

Name _____

Address _____

_____

_____

_____ Postcode _____

You may be mailed as a result of entering this competition

COMP 6